D1250621

MURIEL L. GUBERLET, Assistant Professor Emeritus of English at the University of Washington, has studied the sea and collected seashore animals for many years in many parts of the world. She also worked with her late husband at the Oceanographic Laboratory at Friday Harbor, Washington, and widely studied oceanographic expeditions at the British Museum.

EXPLORERS OF THE SEA

Famous Oceanographic Expeditions

MURIEL L. GUBERLET

With illustrations by Elizabeth L. Curtis

THE RONALD PRESS COMPANY • NEW YORK

Library of Congress Catalog Card Number: 64–13332

PRINTED IN THE UNITED STATES OF AMERICA

To
Connie and Lucy Foster
whose father is a marine
biologist as were both
their grandfathers

Foreword

It is impossible to express individually my thanks for the help and encouragement given me in the preparation of this book by my friends, by members of the oceanographic faculty of the University of Washington, by librarians who sought out obscure books and magazines for my use. Too, my lifelong interest in the sea sustained me in the long arduous task of setting down on paper some developments in oceanography.

Particularly do I acknowledge my debt to those naturalists and oceanographers who have recorded their experiences, achievements, and impressions of the biological and physical features of the sea— its vastness, its complexity, its cruelty, its austere beauty. The writings of these men I have consulted and paraphrased freely.

If *Explorers of the Sea* brings pleasure and a greater understanding of the oceans to readers, all of us will feel amply repaid for the time and work we have put into the book.

Without doubt the most satisfying phase of the study has been discovering the international cooperation among oceanographers— men of many countries unselfishly working together to fit the pieces of the jigsaw puzzle of the sea into their proper places. Together these men will continue to venture into the unknown and to ferret out the plan and purpose of the "One Great Thought" that controls the operation of our universe and preserves the harmonies of Nature.

Muriel L. Guberlet

Seattle, Washington
   January, 1964

Contents

CHAPTER   PAGE

1   MEN DISCOVER THE SEA   3

2   MATTHEW FONTAINE MAURY—PATHFINDER OF THE SEA   12

3   CHARLES WYVILLE THOMSON—THE *Challenger*   32

4   ALEXANDER AGASSIZ—THE *Blake* AND THE *Albatross*   54

5   FRIDTJOF NANSEN—THE *Fram*   74

6   MURRAY AND HJORT—THE *Michael Sars*   97

7   SIR ALISTER HARDY—THE *Discovery I*   115

8   HANS PETTERSSON—THE *Albatross*   134

9   BEEBE, COUSTEAU, AND THE PICCARDS—MAN OBSERVES THE DEPTHS   153

10   ANDERSON AND CALVERT—THE *Nautilus* AND THE *Skate*   176

11   WILLARD BASCOM—THE MOHOLE PROJECT   199

SUGGESTED READINGS   216

INDEX   221

EXPLORERS OF THE SEA

Famous Oceanographic Expeditions

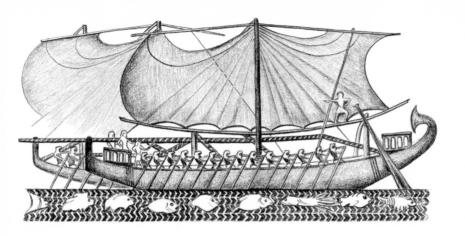

1

Men Discover the Sea

The sea is forever asking questions.

Some eleven hundred years ago, Charlemagne's son Louis stood with his tutor on the seashore looking across a great expanse of water. Louis turned to his teacher and asked, "What is the sea?" The young teacher thought a moment, then answered, "It is the path of the daring, the frontier of land, the decider of continents, the hostelry of rivers, the fountain of rain, a refuge in peril, a treat in pleasure."

Through the centuries thousands of persons have asked the same question, and have received thousands of answers, some of them more specific than Louis' teacher's, some less so. Perhaps never will a definition of the sea be given that will cover all the facets of this great body of water, for its scope is incomprehensible and it probably has a different answer for each inquirer.

Nevertheless, in the last one hundred years a group of men called oceanographers have pitted their brains and their equipment

3

against the vast unknown of the sea in an ever-increasing series of expeditions and studies.

Through "blood, toil, sweat, and tears" these men have supplied partial answers to hundreds of questions about the sea, and have torn away many of the superstitions that surrounded it. Their expeditions have taken them to the far corners of the earth. They have charted the undersea's mountains and valleys; they have studied the movements of the currents; they have probed into the very foundations of the earth to decipher its ancient history; they have gone to the very deepest spot in the sea; and they now aspire to bore through the crust to that never-never land, the mantle, deep in the bosom of the earth. So thorough has been the work of the marine scientists that today the question "What is the sea?" can be answered with far more exactness than could have been done even twenty-five years ago.

It is to describe in some detail a few of these expeditions and to introduce the men who conducted them that this book is written. Each of these expeditions tells a dramatic story of courage, hardship, intellectual curiosity, and high adventure. Yet oceanographers know that great stretches of the sea remain to be studied and the intricate complexities of the water, air, and land have scarcely been comprehended. But by observing a never-ending chain of relationships and environments, they have drawn a picture of the broad features of the seventy-one per cent of the earth's surface covered by water averaging two and a half miles in depth.

Even to oceanographers the sea is still a baffling enigma. Sir Alister Hardy of Oxford, who had studied the sea since his youth, recently said, "To understand the sea is like putting together a huge jigsaw puzzle made up of hundreds of tiny bits which are lying scattered somewhere beneath the surface of the water. To find them we must grope around in the darkness." Then he adds: "Perhaps the ocean seems more mysterious than it really is because we can look at it only from the top, an eternally moving gray-green substance as elusive as a cloud. Except for a brief moment we can not enter it without special equipment. We can not drink it because it is a bitter brine. We can see into it but a little way, but what we see there is intriguing—graceful jellyfish and sleek salmon flashing into view and as quickly disappearing. At night the waters are dotted with tiny lights that dance and glitter like diamonds. For a moment in the open seas many-legged shrimp play on the surface or huge whales and porpoises lift their great bodies on the crest of the waves." Sir Alister concludes: "How we wish the sea would open up for us vertically as it did for the Israelites as they passed through the Red Sea—'and the waters were a wall unto them on their right and on their left.'"

Today we do not expect such a miracle to happen, but slowly year after year the pieces of the puzzle are being fitted into place. Eventually, no one knows when or how, we will understand the sea as well as we do the land.

Certainly man will never be satisfied with present knowledge, for there is something in his very nature that forever drives him forward—to round the next bend in the coastline, to see what lies over the next hill, to venture ever farther from home, to follow the light of the setting sun as it drops over the edge of the sea, to discover the genesis of the earth, even to search for worlds beyond our own.

Since the very earliest times man has attempted to penetrate the sea. Assyrian bas-reliefs show men trying to submerge themselves by sinking on goatskin bellows. About 500 B.C. Alexander the Great is said to have sat in a glass barrel for two months watching the creatures of the deep swim by. Leonardo da Vinci doodled a number of impractical ideas for diving lungs. Elizabethan craftsmen tinkered with leather suits for diving. In the nineteenth century men decked out in steel helmets, weighted shoes and fed air from above dived sixty feet under water. In the last twenty-five years men have descended to the bottom of the sea in a bathysphere and a bathyscaph.

But it was to learn what lay beyond their boundaries and to increase trade that most countries sent out ships. On the walls of Queen Hatshepset's magnificent temple at Der-el-Bahri at Thebes are pictures of an expedition that she sent down the coast of Africa in 1500 B.C. to fetch incense and "odoriferous gums" and to bring back the trees that produced them to be planted at Thebes. The Phoenicians are reputed to have ventured into regions no one else dared to enter. The trade routes of these daring and adventurous navigators were so extensive that they became the distributors of the wines, wheat, barley, dates, and woven stuffs of Egypt and Babylonia. Much of their success at sea was attributed to the strict discipline maintained on their ships. Through their understanding of the winds and tides they probably circumnavigated Africa in 700 B.C.

In 460 B.C. the Carthaginians made a journey through the Straits of Gibraltar and down the west coast of Africa with a fleet of sixty ships, each carrying twenty-five oarsmen on each side. The oars are said to have worked in such perfect unison that the ships looked like caterpillars crawling through the water. The Carthaginians are said also to have set up colonies on the west coast of Africa and even as far away as Madeira and the Canary Islands.

Aristotle, the brilliant Greek scholar who lived in the fourth century B.C., in addition to being a philosopher, logician, and political thinker, was also a biologist with a passion for inquiry into many facts of nature, including a deep interest in the sea. In fact he named a number of seashore animals, many of the names still being used today.

Another Greek philosopher and astronomer named Pytheas in 300 B.C. sailed from Massilia (Marseilles) up the coast of Spain and Gaul for England to buy tin. As he traveled northward Pytheas noticed that when the moon was full, the tides were as high as the tops of the houses; when the moon waned, the tides were only one or two feet high. Pytheas therefore concluded that the moon had something to do with the tides. (At that time most people believed that the tides were caused by the breathing of great sea monsters.) At Ultima Thule, the point farthest north (the Orkney Islands or Iceland, perhaps), Pytheas believed that the sun took a nap for two or three hours a day. He also questioned whether the North Star were really over the North Pole and he made the first attempt to fix latitudes.

The Romans were not much interested in the sea for its own sake. To them sea voyages were necessary evils that were to be avoided whenever land routes were possible. Their one great contribution to marine knowledge was the invention of the anchor. It is significant that their vast literature gives few accounts of the sea itself.

Many centuries passed. During this time the Dark Ages had descended upon Europe. Men feared the restless waters that were said to boil and seethe and were inhabited by horrible monsters; and the unwary might even tumble over the edge of the land and be swallowed up in a dark, deep abyss. Lacking knowledge of the seas, men dreamed up weird stories and filled the vacuum with myths, many of which persisted through centuries. Even today the mythology of the seas far exceeds the knowledge of it.

The only glimmering of interest in the sea was that of the Vikings, who in the eleventh and twelfth centuries built strong ships and voyaged to far places. However, the Vikings added nothing to the understanding of the seas. They were mainly pirates and raiders.

By the middle of the thirteenth century rumors of the fabulous wealth of the Mogul Empire began to filter into southern Europe. Through the lust for gold, jewels, silks, and spices of the East, the Spanish and Portuguese were awakened from a thousand-year sleep. They determined to get their share of these luxuries through exploration and conquest.

No doubt the greatest push toward conquest was given to the Portuguese by Prince Henry, the Navigator. (He was not given this title until 400 years after his death.) Prince Henry, fourth son of King John, was a scholar who lived as simply as a monk in his castle at Sagres near Cape St. Vincent, the most southerly point of Portugal. Henry was an armchair navigator. Yet his imagination ranged the universe and he did much toward changing the thinking of the world.

Although Henry's avowed purpose was to increase the geographical knowledge of the world, spread Christianity, discover the extent of the Mogul Empire, and increase Portuguese trade, his real vision was to chart the unknown by urging a sea route around Africa to India.

His first step toward accomplishing this ambitious program was to improve navigation. To do this he brought together a "faculty of mathematicians, astronomers, pilots, master mariners, scientists, and chroniclers of voyages." This assemblage of learned men established navigation as an exact science. A crude compass and astrolabe, the forerunner of the sextant, were already in use. His engineers next developed the caravel of 100 to 200 tons, an ideal sailing vessel. Henry then turned his attention to the improvement of charts, compasses, and shipboard instruments. The Prince had the greatest difficulties with the superstitious sailors, who refused to venture into the open seas.

When Prince Henry died in 1460, he had succeeded in driving his ships only a thousand miles down the coast of Africa. However, the voyages did not end with Henry's death. Portuguese ships continued to creep down the coast until in 1478 they crossed the equator without disaster.

To the seamen's surprise the seas did not boil, there were no rivers of fire, there were no bottomless abysses at the edge of the world, and the men were able to breathe. With this assurance Bartholomew Diaz decided to press on southward and to venture into the open waters. Through no fault of his own and without displaying any particular skill as a mariner, he rounded the southern tip of Africa in 1488 by being blown around the cape by a hurricane that lasted thirteen days. The King of Portugal named it Cape of Good Hope in honor of Prince Henry, who had hoped for it so long.

Then followed in quick succession the famous voyages of Columbus, Vasco da Gama, Magellan, and many others. Maps changed overnight. Ships crossed and recrossed the oceans, setting Europe in a turmoil. The courageous navigators discovered continents, islands, civilizations, trade routes, strange ways of life. They turned the Atlantic into a highway and opened up a new world geographically, intellectually, and culturally, until the sixteenth and seventeenth centuries became perhaps the most exciting period in the history of the world.

By the end of the seventeenth century the heroic days of surface exploration were over. But this did not mean that there were to be no more exciting oceanic discoveries. Only the goal had changed. By the dawn of the nineteenth century, the extent of the oceans was fairly well known, their boundaries were defined, and the fear of the turbulent waters was gone.

The vast unknown now lay beneath the surface of the waters. Until this time few serious attempts had been made to understand the limitless uncharted depths. Magellan had dropped a 400-fathom (a fathom is six feet) rope over the edge of the ship to measure the ocean's depth. When it did not touch bottom, he concluded that he was over the deepest spot in the seas. In the eighteenth century Captain James Cook tried to plumb the depth of the ocean and to dredge, but he discovered nothing of importance.

During the second quarter of the nineteenth century a few curious German and Scandinavian scientists made biological investigations of the water by dragging through the water a dredge, a rectangular iron frame to which was attached a baglike cotton net to retain the organisms. They also constructed a tow net to catch the multitudes of microscopic plants and animals in the upper layers of the sea—a most significant advance.

As Diaz had been blown around the Cape of Good Hope by chance, so the first definite information about what lived on the bottom of the sea came to man quite by accident. The transatlantic cable, which was laid in 1858 at 1000 fathoms, broke two years later. When it was hauled to the surface for repairs, many weird creatures were clinging to it. What could they be? Surely they were not animals, for no life was thought to exist lower than 300 fathoms and they were like nothing men were familiar with. These little creatures created so much excitement that naturalists and laymen alike were fired with a desire to look deeper under the shimmering waters.

This wide interest led the British Navy and the Royal Society to send the *Challenger* on a four-year cruise—1872 to 1876—around the world to "learn everything about the sea." Even so successful an expedition as the *Challenger's* could not do that, but it was the incentive for many expeditions to be sent to the ends of the earth. The *Challenger* threw open the depths of the ocean to research and has served as the model for most of the oceanic investigations from that day to this.

Oceanography as an organized science really had its beginnings with the *Challenger*. Hoping to study as many phases of the sea as possible, Wyville Thomson, the director, included on his staff zoologists, botanists, and chemists, each one primarily concerned with his own branch of science. Ever since that time oceanographers have been specialists in one of the dozen different branches of marine science.

In most of the early oceanographic expeditions the emphasis was necessarily biological, to describe the animals and to study their distribution. This naturally led to an inquiry into the origin of life in the sea. Then followed studies of the chemical properties of sea water, the penetration of light, the temperature of the water at all levels. The question then arose as to how the contour of the ocean floor and the swing of the currents determine the distribution of the animals. Thus the study of the sea continually became more complex.

It was not until World War II that oceanographic research began on a large scale, however. Increased concern for the seas was largely due to matters of national defense and safety. The seas which had

always protected a country no longer did so.   For better or for worse
with modern transportation the seas no longer isolated countries.
Both for national protection and for increasing knowledge of the sea,
larger, better equipped ships were built. Electronic devices were
installed on them.   Echo sounders, continuous plankton nets, piston
core samplers came into general use in oceanographic research.
Equipment became of utmost importance, for only the instruments
and the minds of men were pitted against the unknown realms of the
seas.

With the help of increasingly efficient equipment, more fundamental and far-reaching projects were undertaken.   To fit the pieces
of the jigsaw puzzle into place required teamwork similar to that of
a group of medical men hovering over a patient before resorting to
an exploratory examination.   The only difference is that the patient
in this case is the immense, heaving, restless sea.

The interrelationships of the winds, currents, chemicals, and
temperature were recognized by Matthew Maury, a philosopher as
well as one of the early oceanographers.   In the 1850's he said that
when we begin to comprehend a harmony and design in the "great
waste of waters" and to realize that every observation is a guide to
the solution of the mystery of the sea and must be considered in the
light of all the other factors—then the study of the sea will become
truly sublime.   Like a motif running through a piece of music,
Maury brings out a divine order in nature.

Yet the men who today are bringing harmony and order out of the
study of the sea are very modest.   Without publicity and without
special reward, they repeat an experiment many times.   To reveal
the truth is their only aim.   Their work is frequently disappointing;
yet after every failure they cheerfully go back to their dredges and
their corers to try once more.

They say with Herman Melville, that famous weaver of sea tales:

> But oh, shipmates, on the starboard side of
> every woe there is a sure delight.
> And higher the top of that delight than the
> bottom of the woe is deep.

Our literature is replete with stories of the fascination the oceans
have always held for men who "go down to the sea in ships."   This
is as true of the modern oceanographer as it was for the Phoenician
sailor, for anyone who has groped beneath the waters in search of a
missing piece of the jigsaw puzzle has been introduced to a world of

endless discoveries, a world of such immense proportions that he will surely have lost forever his narrow, circumscribed view of our planet.

In this book we will follow a few of the men of the past century on their expeditions of discovery, investigate what inspired them to undertake the long difficult journeys, and evaluate their contributions to the understanding of the sea. We can discuss only a few of the expeditions that have made oceanographic history, concentrating on these that had a very specific objective and made a very definite contribution to knowledge.

The book begins with Matthew Maury charting highways across the oceans and ends with the *Mohole,* a project still in the planning stage. These investigations are only the beginning. Countless studies will follow the *Mohole,* for both scientists and governments are aware that the oceans are the last great unexplored region of the earth.

In the not too distant future our very existence may depend upon an understanding and a realization of the riches of the sea. (It has been estimated that the wealth of the oceans far exceeds that of the land.) So pressing is the determination to learn more about the seas that the government of the United States is recommending a wide extension of oceanographic study not only for abstract scientific knowledge, national defense, commerce, and navigation, but for general welfare and food.

Without doubt the sea offers young men opportunities for adventure and travel as exciting and as important to our country as outer space does to the astronauts.

And the sea is here, not a million light years away.

❀   ❀   ❀

Matthew Maury, probably the earliest oceanographer, advanced man's knowledge of the sea by charting highways across the world.

2

Matthew Fontaine Maury —
Pathfinder of the Sea

Ships that pass in the night
And speak to each other in passing.

"How I hate picking cotton," mumbled ten-year-old Matthew
Maury as he worked in the broiling Tennessee sun. "I don't care if it
never gets picked." Angrily he snatched the bolls off the vines and
stuck them into a hollow stump filled with water. However, when
his father discovered the trick he whipped the boy soundly for his

laziness. This only served to make Matthew hate the work more than ever. Then and there he vowed he would never be a cotton planter.

He would get away from the farm as soon as he could and join the United States Navy as his brother had done. The fact that his brother had died of yellow fever while in the Navy did not daunt Matthew. Almost word for word he could repeat the stories his brother had told of far-off places. The games he played and the dreams he dreamed were of the sea. Every tall tree on the plantation became the mast of a ship and he a lookout high in the rigging.

Matthew was born in Fredericksburg, Virginia, January 4, 1806, but when he was five years old the family moved to Tennessee. In the Maury home were books, and music, and love, and a rich family heritage. His father, a very religious man, gave his children such thorough training in the Scriptures, especially the Psalms of David, that all his life Matthew could quote chapter and verse as though he had the Bible before him. Tennessee was very primitive in the early 1800's. In the pioneer school he attended there were no textbooks, no blackboards, and the benches were split logs with peg legs. In a couple of years Matthew had learned all the reading, writing, and arithmetic that the school offered. The only thing that he really enjoyed in school was the singing of geography lessons, which allowed his imagination to roam the world.

When Matthew was twelve he was sent to Harpeth Academy, where he sailed through Latin and reveled in the beautiful logic of mathematics. But even Harpeth could not long satisfy him. He needed broader horizons. He knew his father could not afford to send him to the expensive schools in the East; therefore he decided it was time to join the Navy, which he was sure would give him a chance for an education, opportunities to become a gentleman, and the privilege of serving his country. Without telling his father of his plans he secured a midshipman's appointment through General Sam Houston, whom he had met when he entered Harpeth. Houston had said, "If there's ever anything I can do, let me know. We Virginians must stick together."

When Matthew told his father of his decision, he said, "You'll go as you are with nothing but the clothes on your back. I wash my hands of you. Another son of mine will not lie at the bottom of the sea."

In spite of his father's displeasure, Matthew was determined to accept the appointment. Somehow he got together seventy-five dollars to buy a horse. Riding his "snow white steed" he set off for Virginia to visit with relatives before going on to New York where he was to report to the Frigate *Brandywine*. On that visit he met his beautiful cousin Ann Herndon. At first sight he was completely captivated by her blue eyes, auburn hair, and musical voice. Then he rode on to Washington and New York.

When on August 13, 1823, he approached the *Brandywine*, her dark hull stunned him, towering above the dock like the walls of a canyon. He fingered the warrant in his breast pocket, which read, "And I do strictly charge and require all officers, seamen, and others under his command to be obedient to his orders, and directions." In a daze of pride and patriotism Matthew Maury swore he would be obedient to his orders and he would make the United States and the Navy proud of him.

Luckily the *Brandywine* was particularly honored to take Lafayette home to France after a memorable visit to the United States. As a special mark of appreciation to that early friend of the new republic, midshipmen from twenty-five states had been selected to man the ship. If possible, boys were chosen whose fathers or grandfathers had distinguished themselves in the War of Independence. In this ship Matthew came to know young officers from many parts of the country as well as senior officers such as Charles Morris and David Farragut.

To the great disappointment of everyone, Lafayette suffered from seasickness and gout during the Atlantic crossing and had to stay in his quarters much of the time. But Matthew Maury's enthusiasm was not daunted by Lafayette's illness. He had never seen a ship or the ocean before, so everything was new and exciting to him. Of course he had some difficulty in getting in and out of his hammock. His fellows jeered when he fell flat on the rolling deck, and a bright young lieutenant taunted him for his ignorance of naval terms and naval procedure. But these minor difficulties were soon overcome.

Matthew's only disappointment with the Navy was the lack of educational facilities offered on shipboard. He realized at once he would have to learn navigation, but the only textbook on navigation in the ship's library was in Spanish. Laboriously he dug the principles of navigation from a Spanish text with the aid of a Spanish dictionary. He also learned spherical geometry while walking the decks on his regular watches. To make the problems seem more real, he drew the figures on the cannon balls in the racks.

Late one afternoon as he strode back and forth repeating theorems, Matthew heard a voice behind him say, "So the cannon ball has gone to school." Looking up he saw Lafayette standing behind him. Overcome with embarrassment he stammered, "I expect, sir, you wonder why. It seemed easier to understand on a sphere."

"No, my young friend, I never ask *why*. Only *why not*. *Cur non* is my motto. When I came to America a long time ago to help a new nation fight for a new kind of freedom, my friends asked me, Why? I answered *Cur non*. Then it was nothing but an idea. But an idea worth fighting for." The old general's voice deepened, his eyes flashed.

Bursting with pride that the General had noticed him, Matthew answered, "I guess there is nothing more powerful than an idea. If you believe in it enough, it is worth fighting for. *Cur non* will be my motto too." Lafayette gave the boy a pat on the back and Matthew went on studying the cannon ball.

When the *Brandywine* anchored at Le Havre where the General was to leave the ship, a young lieutenant lowered the ship's flag and handed it to Lafayette. "For you, sir. It couldn't be in better hands." The cheers were thunderous.

With her famous passenger no longer on board the ship seemed empty, the spirit of adventure gone. It's strange what the personality of one man can do, thought Matthew. To fill this void and to give the young sailors experience in many kinds of waters and sailing conditions, the ship was sent to Gibraltar where she was refitted. She returned to New York in 1826.

Matthew's next voyage was on the *Vincennes* which took him around the world (the first American man-of-war to circumnavigate the globe) to the glamorous exotic places his brother had told him of so many years ago—the South Seas, the Sandwich Islands (Hawaii), the Philippines, China. When Matthew walked the streets of these places in cocked hat and sword, he was very conscious that he was representing the United States of America. In spite of his elegant uniform and his sword, the words of the geography lessons sung in the log schoolhouse in Tennessee often flashed through his mind. The backwoods boy from Tennessee was well on his way to becoming an officer and a gentleman.

Matthew was not satisfied with being an officer and a gentleman.

He wanted also to be a scholar. In preparation for his examinations as a Passed Midshipman, he studied in New York for several months. Then back on shipboard he read constantly. At this time he wrote, "It is industry that makes a man. I don't think so much depends upon intelligence as is generally supposed, but industry and steadfastness of purpose, they are the things." Matthew passed the examinations in the mid-rank of his class, a pretty good record for the untrained Tennessee lad.

In recognition of his hard work and his ability to handle men, Maury in June 1831 was appointed sailing master on the *Falmouth* bound for the Pacific Ocean and the Orient. On and on the *Falmouth* sailed, down the coast of the United States, Central America, and South America with a stop at Rio, then around Cape Horn to Valparaiso and Callao, the port of Peru. As the ship made this long slow journey, Maury argued endlessly with the first mate. Couldn't the sailing time be shortened if the winds and currents could be made to aid the ship rather than to hinder it?

Wrinkling his brow and pacing back and forth across his cabin, he felt there must be some sort of pattern to the winds and paths to the currents, if one could but find them. He remembered the morning his brother John had left home to join the Navy. His father had read the psalm about the paths of the sea: "Thou makest man to have dominion over the works of Thy hand—the fowl of the air, the fish of the sea, and whatsoever passeth through the paths of the sea."

Wherever the ship stopped Maury, sextant in hand, made surveys. At Boco del Diables and Labos Rocks off South America he scaled the cliffs to make astronomical and trigonometrical observations. His notebooks soon were filled with page after page of graphs and figures. For three years he served on the *Falmouth*, the *Dolphin*, and the *Patinall* before returning to the United States.

From each port of call he sent a letter to Ann Herndon, to whom he was now engaged, fastening it with a little seal which bore the inscription "Mizpah," that beautiful parting salutation, "The Lord watch between thee and me when we are absent one from the other." Maury had now had almost nine years of continual sea duty. As soon as the ship reached Boston, he secured a leave and hurried to Fredericksburg where he married Ann Herndon. How he looked forward to a few weeks at home with his lovely young wife.

But even as a bridegroom Maury could not be idle for long.

After a few weeks of loafing, he assembled the notes collected on his recent voyage and wrote two articles, "Plan for an Instrument for Finding True Lunar Distance" and "On the Navigation of Cape Horn." Remembering his own need for books when he 'was a fledgling seaman, he also finished a book he had begun some time earlier, *A New Theoretical Treatise on Navigation,* designed to give a young midshipman all the mathematics he needed within one cover. The book, published in 1836, was at once a great success, particularly because it was the first book written by an American naval officer.

When the book was in the hands of the publisher, Maury went by stagecoach to visit his parents in Tennessee. (His father had long since forgotten his irritation with Matthew.) While returning to Fredericksburg, the coach in which he was riding slithered and lurched through the muddy rough roads. Finally it overturned pinning Maury, who had been sitting beside the coachman, beneath it. The gallant young officer had given his seat in the coach to a lady with a baby in her arms. Maury's thigh bone was broken and his knee cap dislocated. The bones did not knit properly and had to be rebroken several times, which meant a long painful convalescence. They never knitted as they should have done, leaving him slightly lame the rest of his life.

Chafing under his enforced idleness and his irritation at not being able to get back to active duty, half in jest and half in bitterness, Maury published a number of articles about the Navy in the *Southern Literary Messenger,* signing them "Henry Bluff, U.S. Navy." Under the title "Scraps from the Lucky Bag" (anything left lying around a man-of-war was tossed into the Lucky Bag) he criticized many practices of the Navy—lack of education for future officers, unpreparedness of the United States for war, need of hydrographic study of the West Coast, need for support of commerce with China, and protection of American fishermen on the whaling grounds.

But a Naval Academy was the thing that he fought for the hardest. He urged that it be established anywhere, "even on the top of the Rocky Mountains," but build it. If the Army needs a headquarters, the Navy needs one too, he argued. For months the identity of Henry Bluff was not discovered. The human gadfly, threatening his own chances of promotion and favor, continued to stir up both admiration and wrath. Whatever the effect upon his own career, his keen observation and caustic wit brought a number of naval problems into the open forum and indirectly resulted in the reorganization of the Navy.

During the next few years Maury asked time and time again for sea duty. Just as often his request was denied. Finally in 1842, almost heartbroken, he gave up the fight and returned to active duty as astronomer and surveyor, work that was to bring him much happiness and much honor. He was given charge of the Depot of Charts and Instruments, which later became the United States Naval Observatory and the Hydrographic Office.

Putting his disappointment behind him, Maury attacked the new assignment with his usual energy and industry. Through industry and steadfastness of purpose he gained the respect and admiration of the world. In the 1850's his name was on the lips of almost every scientist in the world. Even today one can scarcely pick up a book on oceanography or naval science without encountering the name of Matthew Fontaine Maury.

His first job was to reorganize the Depot. One day while this work was going on, a young sailor covered with dust and bent under the weight of old ships' logs staggered into Maury's office and said, "Shall I throw out this old stuff?" An idea flashed into Maury's mind. *Why not* use these records, musty and yellow with age, to reveal the routes followed by ships while crossing the seas? Ever since he had crawled down the coast of South America on the *Falmouth,* he had wondered why there were no charts showing the direction and speed of the winds and currents.

He felt sure the routes then in use were merely tradition, handed down from one generation of seamen to another and followed just because these were the ways ships always went. Most of the routes were crooked and wasteful. For instance, when a vessel sailed from the United States to the Cape of Good Hope, it crossed the Atlantic three times.

Maury was convinced that by setting down on a chart the records of many ships, much safer, shorter, more economical paths across the oceans could be followed. Accordingly he sent out a request for navigators everywhere to help in the improvement of commerce and navigation by turning their log books over to the Observatory. Immediately mariners all up and down the east coast of America rushed to their garrets and brought out old log books and sea journals. These records together with the musty yellowed charts in the Depot became the basis of Maury's famous *Wind and Current Charts*.

Maury explained that "by putting down on a chart the tracks of many vessels on the same voyage, during all seasons, and by projecting along each track the winds and currents daily encountered, together with the latitude and longitude, it was plain that navigators hereafter, by consulting the charts, would have for their guide the results of the combined experience of all ships whose tracks were recorded."

On the charts (twenty-four records were to be taken each day, some of them every two hours) he asked certain conditions be noted by using colors and symbols—a comet tail for wind, an arrow for currents, Arabic numerals for temperature, Roman numerals for barometer readings, broken and dotted lines for months, and colors for the four seasons. He felt sure that by using these charts a totally inexperienced navigator would be able to start out on a voyage with as much confidence as though he had made it a hundred times. Optimistically Maury foresaw the routes becoming heavily traveled turnpikes.

The Navy was so impressed by the possibilities of the charts that the Secretary asked Maury to read a paper explaining them before the National Institute. The paper, "Wind and Current Charts of the North Atlantic," aroused so much interest that seamen everywhere were talking about it. However, Maury was not satisfied with the charts; he knew the information in the old logs and sea chests was not complete, so he decided to enlist help in collecting data. Mr. Upsher, Secretary of the Navy, authorized all public carriers to gather daily information on latitude and longitude; hourly rate of the currents; speed and direction of the winds; temperatures; barometric pressure before, during, and after a storm; and other phenomena such as fogs, whales, birds, islands, and shoals sighted, and errors in earlier charts.

The sea captains were also asked to throw into the water tightly corked bottles with instructions for their return to the ships' headquarters. The purpose of these "mute little navigators" was to estimate the course and speed of the current which had carried the bottles on their way. To encourage the taking of these data, Maury offered a free copy of the charts to all ships cooperating.

"It's just a fool scheme of some crackpot in Washington," the ship masters complained. They fussed and fumed and refused to take the readings. A whole year passed before a single record came in. But Maury could wait. There were other projects that he was burning to investigate.

Getting almost no responses from merchant vessels, Mr. Upsher ordered all naval ships to make these observations every two hours. The Navy men complained as loudly as the merchant men had done, but a Navy order was a Navy order, and they had no choice but to obey. What was the surprise of the officers to find that by following the charts the far corners of the world were brought closer together by many days. Everywhere routes were shortened.

For example, the average sailing time between Rio and New York was cut from 55 to 35 days. And between New York and San Francisco around Cape Horn, a distance of 14,000 miles, the time was cut from 183 days to 135 days. The route between New York and San Francisco became the great racecourse of the oceans for clipper ships exhibiting glorious trials of speed and prowess. One of the most exciting races was won by the *Flying Fish*, which made the journey in 93 days and 20 hours. The shortened route greatly stimulated the Gold Rush to California in 1849.

Maritime nations all over the world began to see the great promise of the shortened routes. Nine years after the first *Wind and Current Charts* were sent out, a thousand navigators were busy night and day recording data according to a uniform plan. By this time the charts embodied the results of 265,298 days of observation. Best of all there was no expense with the work because most ships had the instruments on board for making the observations.

In 1858 Captain Phinney of the American merchant ship *Gertrude* wrote to Maury:

> For myself I am free to confess that for many years I commanded ships and although never insensible to the beauties of nature upon land or sea, I feel that until I took up your work, I had been traversing the seas blindfolded. . . . I did not think; I did not know the amazing and beautiful combination of all the works of Him whom you so beautifully call 'The First Great Thought.' . . . I feel that aside from the pecuniary profit to myself from your labors, you have done me good as a man. You have taught me to look above, around, and beneath me and to recognize God's hand in every element by which I am surrounded. . . . I am grateful for this personal benefit."

Never before had such a corps of men worked together in any phase of physical science; never before had men shown such interest with regard to ocean highways. Maury now dreamed of a universal system of meteorological observations on land and sea.

He wrote hundreds of letters to scientists all over the world urging them to support such a scheme. (How he wished he had one of those new-fangled mechanical machines for writing letters.)

The outcome of these compelling letters and of Maury's reputation was a conference attended by representatives of all the maritime countries of the world in Brussels in August 1853. At the first session of the conference Maury was called upon to explain the purpose of the meeting. When he had finished his plea, men of nine nations stood and applauded "the representative of the youngest nation among them."

That night Maury wrote to his wife: "Rarely has there been such a sublime spectacle presented to the scientific world; all the nations agreeing to unite and cooperate in carrying out one system of philosophical research with regard to the sea. They may be enemies in all else, but here they are to be friends." The results of the conference were the adoption of an abstract log for the use of men-of-war of all nations and one for merchant men to use in the system of cooperative observations. In his enthusiasm Maury said, "Every ship that navigates the high seas with these charts and blank abstract logs on board may henceforth be regarded as a floating laboratory, a temple of science."

Maury had indeed become the "Pathfinder of the Sea." From the thousands of reports that came in, he continued to chart routes until there were detailed courses across the North and South Atlantic, the North and South Pacific, and the Indian Ocean. He explained the efficiency of the charts by saying, when one looks from the shore and sees a ship disappear on the horizon the common idea is that she is bound over a trackless waste and the chances of seeing another ship sailing in the same direction are very slim. Yet the winds and currents are becoming so well known and understood that two ships going from New York to San Francisco would follow so nearly the same course that the captains could salute each other or have tea together almost at will.

Recognition came to Maury from many quarters. He was given a Master's degree by North Carolina and an LL.D. by Columbia University. A clipper ship was named in his honor. The Insurance Underwriters of America gave him a purse of $5,000. The Secretaries of the Navy praised his work. In spite of his fame, he was not rewarded by advancement in rank.

Probably the thing that Matthew Maury had fought for the hard-

est came into being in 1845 when the Naval Academy was established in Annapolis, Maryland. Through the urging of Navy Secretary George Bancroft, the historian, old Fort Severn was turned
over to the Navy, and Maury had the honor of being called "The
Father of Annapolis."

With a burning passion to spread information about the sea,
Maury asked himself why not assemble the great store of information he had gathered in compiling the *Wind and Current Charts* into
a book which would treat the whole economy of the sea—the circulation of the water and the atmosphere; the temperature and depth of
the seas; the salts, the chemicals and the inhabitants of the sea.

So sandwiched between a hundred and one duties he wrote his
famous work, *The Physical Geography of the Sea*, which was published in 1855. In England the book was so popular it ran into nine-
teen editions; in the United States it was printed in nine editions. It
was translated into Dutch, German, French, Spanish, and Norwegian
and was used as a textbook in several naval schools on the Continent.
Time and time again Maury revised the book, adding or rejecting
material as new information was found or old ideas were discarded.
His only wish was to keep pace with the latest findings of marine
science. "I am wedded to no theories and do not advocate the
doctrines of any particular school. Truth is my objective," he wrote.

No matter on what subject Maury wrote, he injected a poetic
style and a reverence for the amazing harmonies of the natural
world. His delightful style is shown in the opening sentences of
the chapter on the Gulf Stream: "There is a river in the ocean. In
the severest droughts it never fails, and in the mightiest flood it never
overflows. Its banks and bottom are of cold water while its current
is of warm. The Gulf of Mexico is its fountain, and its mouth is
the Arctic Ocean. It is the Gulf Stream. There is in the world no
other such majestic flow of waters. Its current is more rapid than
the Mississippi or the Amazon and its volume is a thousand times
greater." (Its volume is three thousand times greater than the
Mississippi.)

He continues in the same vein by saying, "The indigo blue waters
of the Gulf Stream are so distinctly marked that one half of a vessel
may be seen floating in Gulf Stream water while the other half is in
ordinary water. It seems as though the Gulf Stream feels itself
superior and does not wish to associate with the common water."

Using an interesting simile, Maury likens the Gulf Stream to a hot water furnace. The Gulf of Mexico and the Caribbean Sea are the cauldrons; the Gulf Stream the connecting pipe; the great Banks of Newfoundland to the shores of Europe the basement or hot air chamber in which the pipes flare out to present a large cooling system. As the warm water reaches the shores of Europe, the west wind picks it up and disperses it "in a most benign manner."

More specifically this wonderful stream of warm water sets out on its long journey from the Gulf of Mexico across the Strait of Florida, up the coast of the United States to Cape Hatteras. Here it turns northeast to the Great Banks of Newfoundland. Beyond this point it travels east across the Atlantic Ocean, dividing into three currents, one to Norway, one to England, and one to the west coast of Africa. Then it turns back toward the Gulf of Mexico and makes the long trip all over again. In the region of Cape Hatteras the Stream is about 75 miles wide, 114 fathoms deep, and travels at the rate of three knots. However, depending upon many conditions, it varies widely in its proportions. In the winter at the surface the temperature may be 80° F. and at a depth of 3000 feet the thermometer will probably stand at 57° F.

Even after its journey across the Atlantic Ocean and contact with cold northern currents, the Gulf Stream raises the temperature of England and other countries of Western Europe as much as twenty degrees over places of like latitudes on the North American coasts. Maury believed that the heat discharged over the Atlantic by the Gulf Stream can raise the whole column of atmosphere that rests over France and the British Isles from the freezing point to summer heat. Poetically he says, "It is the soothing influence of this stream that clothes the shores of England in a gown of green while Newfoundland is shrouded in a mantle of snow and ice."

The Gulf Stream not only modifies climates. It is also sometimes called the "weather breeder," for furious gales of wind sweep along with it, and the fogs of Newfoundland which endanger navigation in the winter are thought to owe their origin in that cold sea to the immense amounts of warm water brought by the Gulf Stream. Besides tempering the weather of Europe and bringing storms, this fabulous ocean river affects the number and quality of fish (the choicest varieties avoid it), the conditions of commerce and navigation, and for a number of years served as a measure of longitude.

But what, asked Maury, sets this great body of water in motion? What forces it forward thousands of miles without apparent impulse? After considering many theories and after long and careful study, he concluded that the movement is due in large part to the winds, to differences in specific gravity or relative density of the water, and to the rotation of the earth. These forces together cause the fresher lighter water to rise to the surface and the denser saltier water continually to sink. In summary he says that the salt left behind when the trade winds pick up the surface waters as they blow over the tropics must be carried away from the trade wind region to be mixed again with the other waters of the sea. The moving of this water in response to the forces of the spinning earth then is one of the chief duties assigned to the Gulf Stream. In short, he believed that it is the law of matter in motion that controls the Gulf Stream in its course. (The wind, topography, and the rotation of the earth are now thought to determine the course and speed of the Gulf Stream.)

Since Maury was wedded to no theory and was looking only for the truth, he concludes his discussion of the Gulf Stream by saying, "In the present state of our knowledge concerning this wonderful phenomenon—for the Gulf Stream is one of the most marvelous things in the ocean—we can do little more than conjecture. But he who contemplates the sea must look upon it as a part of the exquisite machinery by which the harmonies of Nature are preserved."

With each burst of creative energy, Maury spent the night pacing his living room floor. No amount of urging would make him go to bed. Now he was trying to explain the salts in the sea. Once more he admitted he was working on a hypothesis as a cornerstone. Yet with all experimental work, he said, a hypothesis deserves respectful consideration until it has been proved false or a more logical explanation has been presented.

Maury felt sure that the sea has a uniform salinity with the minerals in as constant proportion as are the gases in the atmosphere. This uniformity in ocean water is brought about by the continuous mixing of the water and is evidenced by the fact that a sample of water from the Pacific Ocean is almost identical with one from the Atlantic or the Indian Ocean. As an example of the thorough mixing Maury compared the waters from the Red Sea, where there is almost no rain, where no rivers run into it, and where there is extreme evaporation, with the Mediterranean, into which many rivers discharge soluble matter and where the evaporation is only moderate. Yet the waters of these two completely different seas are almost exactly alike. Truly, the waters are from the seven seas.

For the chemicals to mix so thoroughly, Maury believed that there must be a system of circulation as orderly and as regular as the circulation of the human blood. Maury's tests showed the solid part of the water amounted to about three and one-half per cent of the weight of the water or one-half ounce to the pound. Over three-fourths of the chemicals of the sea is common salt (sodium chloride) with smaller percentages of magnesium, potassium, calcium, sulphate, and minute traces of almost all the other chemical elements.

The circulation is set in motion, he said, when "the sea breeze plays upon the surface; it converts the fresh water into vapor and leaves the solid matter behind. The new surface water thus becomes specifically heavier and sinks."

As the fresh surface water is carried into the atmosphere and the salt-laden water sinks, a movement or circulation is set up. Maury's hypothesis was that it is the salt in the sea that makes circulation of the water or the movement of currents possible. These currents travel from one end of the earth to the other with perfect regularity and order, resulting in the water becoming as well mixed as though it had been shaken up in the same bottle.

Maury believed, too, that animals assist in bringing about changes in density and therefore in the circulation of the water by extracting lime from it for making their shells and building up coral reefs and atolls. For example the currents act as "hod carriers" by bringing lime to the tiny coral animals as they construct the beautiful Polynesian Islands. Maury believed too that there are regular and appointed channels through which the water travels both in surface and deep sea currents, and that "every drop of water in the sea is as obedient to law and order as are the members of the heavenly host in the remotest regions of space."

To answer the difficult question of where the salts came from Maury turned to the Bible. From his childhood he had believed that the universe was planned and guided by "One Great Thought," and that the Bible was the revelation of that plan to man. For this reason he did not agree with Darwin and other scientists of the day that the salts of the sea were derived from the rains and the rivers by dissolving them from the rocks and soil. (According to present day theories, most of the solid material dissolved in the sea originated from the weathering of the crust of the earth.)

To Maury a more logical reasoning was that the sea was salt from the beginning. Certainly as early as the Fifth Day of Creation when, according to the Book of Genesis, the sea was commanded to "bring forth abundantly the moving creatures that hath life." In the light of that divine order the animals of the sea have been dependent upon salt water since the beginning of time.

Naturally some of Maury's theories were early challenged, particularly his explanation of the salts of the sea. These criticisms, however, did not lessen the estimation of his greatness as a pioneer in the field of oceanography. Today, a hundred years after Maury wrote *The Physical Geography of the Sea,* some of his concepts appear unscientific and unrealistic. Still the book remains a model of popular science, written by a man who was possessed of all the knowledge of his time and afire with enthusiasm for marine research. Certainly he was a man of vision. At the same time he applied tremendous energy and industry in trying to make his theories practical realities.

Having presented his hypothesis of the origin of the salts of the sea to the world, Maury again paced the floor. His wife, ever watchful of his health, tried to persuade him to rest, but his fertile brain would not let him stop working. This time he was pondering a very practical and immediate problem: What was the bottom of the sea like?

There was at this time much talk about laying a telegraphic cable across the Atlantic Ocean. If a cable were to be laid, men must know the contour of the ocean floor, the depth of the water, and the possible life in the water. Even in the middle of the nineteenth century, the bottom of the ocean was almost as much a mystery as it had been in Aristotle's time. It was high time man discarded the myths about the sea and learned the truth, Maury insisted.

Surely man's ingenuity would find some way to plumb the ocean's depth and to unlock its long kept secrets, he argued. Through the ages men had made many ingenious and beautiful devices for this purpose. The ancient Greeks had tried to immerse themselves in glass barrels as "lookout capsules." Magellan had attempted to measure the depth of the ocean by dropping a 400-fathom rope over the side of the *Trinidad.* In 1768 Captain James Cook attempted to measure the temperatures of the water and the depth of the ocean. More recently men had tried to fathom the ocean depths by exploding gunpowder and estimating the depth by the time that it took the echo to travel back to the surface. But none of these attempts had yielded information of any value.

In 1849 the United States Navy authorized three ships to help Maury with the wind and current investigations. Maury persuaded Congress to let him combine the chart work with soundings that he hoped would give information about the depth of the water and other conditions of the deep seas.

This permission having been granted, two Navy lieutenants on the schooners *Taney* and *Dolphin* attempted to reach bottom by dropping weighted hemp lines to depths of 34,000 and 39,000 feet. Neither of the men was certain that the rope had touched bottom because the lines either broke, deep currents carried off the surface float, or the weight, if not lost before reaching the bottom, was too heavy to be brought back to the surface.

One afternoon, while Maury was slumped in his office chair considering this knotty question, Passed Midshipman John M. Brooke, a graduate of the first class at the new Naval Academy, reported for duty at the Naval Observatory. To whet his imagination, Maury gave him the problem of how to measure the depth of the sea and find out what the bottom was like. In a few days Brooke was back in Maury's office with a sheaf of sketches. His plan was to wind ten thousand fathoms (a fathom is six feet) of sounding twine on drums marked at 100-fathom intervals with red bunting. At the end of the twine a cannonball weighing 32 or 64 pounds would be attached as a plummet.

The cannonball would be thrown from the ship held as stationary as possible and the twine allowed to run out as fast as it would. On striking the bottom the shot would detach itself from the line as evidence that it had reached the bottom and the depth would be indicated by counting the number of bands of red bunting reeled off. Brooke hoped that bottom materials, if any, would adhere to a piece of soap or tallow in a little cup at the end of the rod from which the shot had been detached.

Maury listened to Brooke's description of the sketches without saying a word. Then he shouted, "You've got it! Detachment of the cannonball. That's the secret. It will prove the bottom has been reached and the rod to which the cup is fastened will strike with such force it will sink into the bottom and pick up any material it comes in contact with. Good boy! Why didn't we think of this before?"

Brooke and Maury hurried to the instrument maker to urge him to build the sounding device at once. The next time the *Dolphin* went to sea it carried John Brooke's sounding device. Great was the excitement when it was first tested. So little was known of the sea bottom that the first material brought up in the cup was very disappointing. It was nothing but soft yellow brown clay.

A sailor was about to throw it back overboard when one of the lieutenants stopped him, saying, "Maybe we had better take it home to the boss. At least it will show we tried." Indifferently he labeled the material and put it on a shelf. The young officers tested the device several times. Each time the cup brought up the same sticky, claylike material.

When the ship returned to the United States, Maury was not at all impressed with the bottom material. But he sent it to Professor Bailey, a famous microscopist at West Point. After long and minute examination, the professor declared the material was the microscopic shells of tiny one-celled animals called foraminifera. Although Professor Bailey did not believe the animals had lived or died at these depths, he felt sure these little shells might be guides to new and valuable knowledge. He was so excited that he urged Maury to get whalers, sea captains—everybody, everywhere—to collect deep sea samples.

Maury did not agree with the professor that the material was the skeletons of living creatures, for he believed the great pressures of the water would prevent animals from living in deep water. But, following his old motto of *Cur non*, he persuaded the Navy to furnish the twine and the cannonballs to any vessel willing to sound the bottom of the sea. Soon ships everywhere were measuring the depth of the water and hauling cups of claylike ooze, as the calcareous remains of these small animals is called, off the ocean floor. With this simple device samples of soft claylike ooze were brought up from depths of more than two miles from many parts of the world.

Nothing had caused so much excitement for a long time. Where did these tiny creatures come from? Had they lived in the surface water and sunk to the bottom or had they lived in some remote part of the ocean and been carried about by the currents? Some people asked (as they still do today) what's the use of this kind of research?

Maury retorted by asking Benjamin Franklin's famous question, "What is the use of a newborn babe?" Indignantly Maury added,

Every physical fact, every expression of nature, every feature of the earth, the work of any and all of these agents that make the world what it is, and as we see it, is interesting and instructive. Until we get hold of a group of physical facts, we do not know what practical bearings they may have, though right-minded people know they contain many precious jewels which science or the expert hand of philosophy will not fail to bring out polished and bright and beautifully adapted to man's purpose. [What was the use of that first crude flying machine at Kittyhawk?]

Brooke's sounding device was so successful that it was in general use for many years and was a great step forward in the study of the sea. From a piece of tallow on the end of a sounding line to today's heavy dredges that sweep from the ocean floor everything in their path was but a short step.

Later and later at night Maury worked (his wife dozing in her chair at his side) and longer and more complex became the chapters of *The Physical Geography of the Sea*. When the book was finished, it was a testimonial to his hard work, his keen observations, his insight into the myriad phases of the sea, and his ability to enlist the cooperation of scientists, ship masters, and ordinary seamen. With such a mind and such a personality, Maury was drawn ever deeper into world oceanography.

On both sides of the Atlantic he read papers, attended conferences, advised governments, and counseled business men. New editions of his book continued to be printed and translated into half a dozen languages. Everywhere he became known as the Great Oceanographer. Largely through confidence in Maury's wind and current charts, thousands of ships crossed and recrossed the world from the Arctic to the Antarctic, from Europe to Asia, until the period preceding the Civil War became a second great age of exploration and investigation.

One Atlantic ship captain said that never before had so many persons exhibited such concern for the study of the sea. Yet no matter how involved in work Matthew Maury was or what the hour of the day or night, he was never too busy or too tired to listen to a visitor. The talk might contain the germ of an idea, he said. Success, fame, and happiness were his, yet he was very modest. He did not claim to have discovered anything. "I only bring together," he said. "Sometimes I do become the mouthpiece of these observations and proclaim to the world what they mean to me."

During the years in which he had been so busy directing the

work of the Observatory and carrying on his researches, he had given little thought to advancement in rank in the Navy, remaining a lieutenant year after year. In 1855 by an act of Congress, a Retiring Board was appointed to promote the general efficiency of the Navy, to make a careful investigation of its personnel, and to report "those found incapable of performing promptly and efficiently their duties ashore and afloat." Without a hearing of any kind Maury, along with many other officers, was placed on a "reserved on leave of absence" list. "Clearing out the dead wood," the Navy said. However, the orders said Maury was to continue on his present duty.

Now Maury's indignation was aroused. "Retired to increase the efficiency of the Navy," the ultimate sarcasm. After thirty years in the service of his country this was a grievous wrong. He realized that his work had upset many old naval traditions and he had locked horns with a number of officers of superior rank. Perhaps, too, it was due to jealousy that he, a mere lieutenant, should have established a reputation as a scientist. Could it also be a slur on his lameness, he asked. In spite of his dreadful hurt, he insisted that, "If I had to choose between being a commander or a captain and originating *The Wind and Current Charts,* I'd take the charts."

After two years of intercession of hundreds of influential friends who were shocked at this treatment, among them General Sam Houston, Maury was restored to active duty and raised to the rank of Commander. The night he received the letter telling of his promotion, with his large, devoted family gathered around him, he quoted his favorite Psalm: "O, Lord, our Lord, how excellent is Thy name in all the earth. What is man that Thou art mindful of him. . . . Thou makest him to have dominion over the works of Thy hands. . . . The fowl of the air and the fish of the seas and whatsoever passeth through the paths of the sea."

That same year, 1858, saw the completion of a 1600-mile long cable laid on the transatlantic plateau plotted on John Brooke's soundings. With Cyrus Field, the principal sponsor of the project, Matthew Maury and John Brooke shared in its success.

The rumblings of the Civil War were now heard everywhere. Maury was born in Virginia and brought up in Tennessee, so naturally his sympathies were with the South, although he was not a disunionist. With the storm clouds gathering, he wrote: "What a comfort the sea is." But even the comfort of the sea was not to be his for long. Three days after Virginia seceded from the Union in 1861, Maury forwarded to President Lincoln his "resignation from the service in which he had spent so many happy and profitable years." He threw his fortune in with Virginia, becoming head of the coast, river, and harbor defenses. He invented an electric torpedo for harbor defense and went to England in behalf of the South. For eight years the Civil War and its aftermath were to bring Maury much unhappiness.

In 1868 he returned to the United States eager to get back to work. He accepted a professorship at Virginia Military Institute where he continued to write and lecture. Although he did a great deal of research in meteorology and agriculture, his marine work was at an end. He was offered the presidency of half a dozen colleges and many honors came to him, but he was a sad and broken man. Today a building at the Naval Academy bears his name. And at the head of all charts issued by the United States Hydrographic Office are the words, "Founded upon the researches made and the data collected by Lieutenant M. F. Maury, U. S. Navy."

Maury died February 1, 1873. On his monument is the following inscription:

> Matthew Fontaine Maury
> Pathfinder of the Sea.
> The genius who first snatched
> From ocean and atmosphere
> The secrets of the Sea.

*   *   *

The paths that Matthew Maury charted across the oceans guided the *Challenger,* the first great oceanographic expedition ship, around the world.

3

Charles Wyville Thomson — *The* Challenger

What seas, what shores, what gray rocks and what islands.

In 1871 Wyville Thomson, a well-known Scotch naturalist, was asked by the Royal Society to make a four-year trip around the world as director of an expedition to study the deep seas. To travel around the world, to visit all the places he had dreamed of, to see new sights, to explore the depths of the oceans. What could be more wonderful, he asked himself.

He realized that he would be a pioneer in the exciting new field of oceanography which everyone, both scientist and layman, was talking about. But he was not sure the trip was for him. Thomson was in an agony of indecision. He was forty years of age. His health was not good. He had a wife and son and a responsible university position which would be hard to leave. But more than anything he wanted to help solve the mysteries of the great unknown seas. For weeks he argued the question with himself. Finally his desire overcame his reason and he took the post, probably one of the most fortunate decisions in biological history.

Not until ten or fifteen years before this time had there been any serious interest in what lay beneath the surface of the waters, what the oceans were really like. Matthew Maury had recently plotted paths across the wide seas and had published his *Physical Geography of the Sea,* which had opened up whole new worlds to the seamen of Europe and America. Charles Darwin's revolutionary theory of evolution, in which he maintained that life on this planet had developed from the tiny one-celled animals in the sea, was still in the fore of men's minds.

Inquisitive young scientists in many countries were intrigued with studying the nature of living things particularly in the sea and were quietly carrying on experiments in their laboratories. They realized that the seas were almost totally unexplored and that the little man did know about the waters that cover almost three-fourths of the earth's surface had been reported by geographers or by superstitious and ignorant fishermen or trawlers who tossed back into the sea everything unfamiliar or strange, believing it was a devil that would bring them ill luck.

Even the most advanced scientific thinkers such as Edward Forbes believed that it would be as impossible for plants and animals to exist under the great pressure of the water, the lack of food, the darkness, and the other adverse conditions of the deep "as to live in a vacuum or in fire." For these reasons they thought that life in the sea must be confined to the narrow strip of land along the shore and that at a depth of 300 fathoms the sea was a desolate waste. Forbes had said, "As we descend deeper and deeper, the inhabitants become more and more modified, and fewer and fewer, indicating an approach toward an abyss where life is either extinguished or exhibits but a few sparks to mark its extinguishing presence."

In 1858 the transatlantic cable had been laid at a depth of 1000 fathoms. The route had been checked with John Brooke's sounding device, but that had given little real information about the nature of life on the bottom of the sea. Two years later the cable broke and had to be hauled to the surface for repairs. To the great surprise of everyone, the cable was covered with strange, weird creatures no one had seen before. This raised all sorts of questions. What was the sea floor like; what was the chemical content of the water; what effect would animals have upon the rubber through which the cable passed; and what was the temperature of the water?

A few Norwegian scientists had perhaps the most active interest in the sea and had dredged at 300 to 400 fathoms and had found life to be abundant at these depths. Michael Sars, a Norwegian naturalist, had even dredged at 700 fathoms. In one dredge he had obtained a number of feather stars, distant relatives of the starfish, a group of animals in which Wyville Thomson had made considerable study. Sars invited Thomson to Christiania (Oslo) to see this unusual animal. The work of the Norwegians convinced Thomson that it was time for the British to find out for themselves something about the animals that lived in the dark cold waters.

As soon as he got home, he asked W. B. Carpenter, a vice-president of the Royal Society, to visit him in Edinburgh.

"What do you really think about the furor the discovery of deep sea animals is causing?" asked Carpenter.

"My own conviction is that the sea is the land of promise for the naturalist. It is the last remaining region where endless novelties are waiting for someone to gather them," answered Thomson.

"What had we better do?" inquired Carpenter, catching some of Thomson's enthusiasm.

"Use your influence at headquarters in London to get the Royal Society to send a small vessel equipped with a dredge and other instruments to sea, preferably off the north coast of Scotland." (A dredge is a rectangular or triangular frame to which a baglike net is attached. As this is dragged across the bottom of the sea by a slowly moving ship, it picks up materials in its path.)

The Royal Society and the Admiralty (the Navy) agreed to this proposal, and in the summer of 1868 Thomson and Carpenter knocked about in the rough seas between Scotland and the Faroe Islands in the *Lightning*, a cranky little boat. During the months of July and August the men were able to work only nine days because of stormy weather. However, they made remarkable discoveries. They dredged at 600 fathoms and at this depth found not only simply organized animals but more highly developed creatures including the bony fishes. During this trip they also perfected the registering thermometer, so constructed that the bulb was protected from extreme pressure by enclosing it in an outer shell of glass with fluid and a bell of vapor between them, making the taking of water temperatures an accurate and routine procedure.

When the *Lightning* got back to Scotland, the men were besieged with questions and the Admiralty was so pleased with their findings that during the summers of 1869 to 1870 the *Porcupine* was turned over to them. This ship was much better suited for deep sea study than was the *Lightning* and the weather was much better. Thomson managed to dredge animals from a depth of 2435 fathoms or more than two and a half miles, many of them belonging to species hitherto unknown. He also toppled the old idea that sea water had a constant temperature of 4° C. or 39° F. Instead he found that it was warm or cold at all depths depending upon the layer of water from which it came. More important, perhaps, was the confirmation that near the surface of the water were suspended millions of tiny plants and animals so small that they could not be seen with the unaided eye. To the average layman these discoveries were almost fantastic.

To bring the exciting story of these fact-finding trips to the world, Wyville Thomson wrote *The Depths of the Sea*, which was successful immediately. This remarkable book is still widely read and is regarded as the first textbook on oceanography. Interest in the sea was at a high pitch. Wyville Thomson was a famous man.

The investigation of the seas now became a race between several countries. The British, not to be outdone by the Scandinavians, decided to use public funds to procure a ship for a four-year study of "every phase of the sea." They would equip it with the most modern instruments and staff it with the best scientists in England. The *Challenger*, a warship-type sailing vessel of 2,306 tons built in 1851 with an auxiliary steam engine and a twin propeller, was bought for this adventure.

Captain Nares of the Admiralty, "a devilish good fellow," a man of wide experience and in sympathy with scientific research, was selected captain. As was to be expected, Wyville Thomson was asked to be the scientific director.

Wyville Thomson was born May 5, 1830, at his ancestral home on the Firth of Forth, where the family had been active in the town and neighborhood for generations. Wyville, a bright handsome boy with an active mind, attended Marchisten School where he particularly enjoyed reading the Latin poets. He entered the University of Edinburgh at sixteen as a medical student.

Yet he was never deeply interested in medicine. He much preferred zoology, botany, and geology. Often when he should have been sitting over his physiology or anatomy books, he was tramping through the woods or along the shores in search of plants or animals. During the third year of medical school, because of ill health, he left the university without taking a degree.

"As a naturalist I will be able to spend much time out of doors," he rationalized. "A doctor has to work too hard to suit me. I want some leisure." But that leisure never came. Because of his wide knowledge of science, not only of zoology but of chemistry and physics as well, he was appointed in quick succession as a Lecturer in Botany at the University of Aberdeen; Professor of Natural History in Queen's College, Cork; Professor of Zoology and Botany in Belfast; and at this time was Professor of Natural History in the University of Edinburgh.

His students adored him. He was a superb teacher, speaking always without notes and illustrating his lectures with living specimens. On Saturday mornings, with a collecting box thrown over his shoulder, he strode off across the fields with a group of students, stopping every few minutes to point out an unusual animal or plant. To top off a perfect day, this genial, charming man entertained the students at his home in the evening with songs, games, and food.

In spite of his heavy schedule of teaching, field trips, judging flower shows, and entertaining, Thomson found time to do marine research. He had recently written a very detailed paper on the rosy feather star, beautifully illustrated with his own drawings.

It was this paper that brought him the invitation to visit Michael Sars in Christiania and to the attention of the Royal Society, which resulted in his cruises on the *Lightning* and the *Porcupine*. Then he had accepted the invitation to direct the scientific work of the *Challenger*. This he did fully realizing that the trip would be a challenge to him too, both from a scientific and a health standpoint.

Before the old warship-type of vessel could be used as a research ship, it had to be remodeled. During the summer of 1872 Nares and Thomson spent almost every waking hour on the docks at Sheerness overseeing the remodeling. The main deck was made into laboratories and workrooms. Space was reserved for the storing of specimens and preserving spirits (wine was used for this purpose), microscopes, preserving jelly, tanks, bottles, and countless other supplies necessary for a four-year cruise. Large areas on deck were given over to the storing of nets, trawls, dredges, and rope—hundreds of miles of it.

Comfortable sleeping rooms as well as a chart room and lounge were provided for the officers and scientists. In the sitting room were a desk, easy chairs, and bookcases filled with old home favorites. Nor did they forget the galley and messrooms, where roast beef, Yorkshire pudding, and plum pudding would be served. In the hold of the ship space was reserved for cattle, pigs, and chickens to provide fresh meat.

Such a happy, busy summer neither Nares nor Thomson had ever spent. All was ready by December 6, 1872. Shiny with new paint and decked with colorful flags, the *Challenger* was host to the Lords of the Admiralty and the Committee of the Royal Society. With Wyville Thomson as master of ceremonies, sixty men sat down to dinner in the wardroom equipped as a general mess. The food was good, the spirits were high, and the toasts gay as the men predicted the success of the expedition and its effect upon science, England, and the times.

Fired with great patriotism and hoping desperately to fulfill the difficult mission of learning "everything about the sea," Wyville Thomson, John Murray, Henry Nottidge Moseley, J. Y. Buchanan, A. von Willemoes Suhm, J. J. Wilde, William Sterling, and their assistants, together with 223 ship's officers and men, stood on the deck of the *Challenger* on December 21, a cold, raw, rainy morning. As the lines were cast off and the ship moved away from the shore, many a man had a lump in his throat and a tear in his eye as he waved to his loved ones whom he would not see again for nearly four years.

The bad weather dogged the ship all through the English Channel. When it reached Kent, most of the scientists left the ship and traveled overland to Portsmouth. On Christmas Day in the Bay of Biscay, the *Challenger* wallowed and creaked and pitched so much many of the seamen, instead of eating roast goose and plum pudding, lay sick and miserable in their bunks. Those who were able to stand up worked endlessly to keep the ship from foundering and the scientific equipment from breaking loose from its moorings. Everyone, with the possible exception of Wyville

Thomson, cursed the ship and the weather and would gladly have turned around and gone home.

But Wyville Thomson was not discouraged. He knew that the storm would soon blow itself out. He knew too that his first job was to determine what animals lived in specific areas. The second job was to learn why these animals live where they do—in other words, what were the organic and inorganic factors of their environment. He realized too that the animals they would collect would be but a minute fraction of the population within a given area, for the dredge would make but a pin prick in the vast seas.

Even when the storm abated the men's problems were not over. They were not used to the techniques of dredging in deep seas and were helpless trying to handle the gear in the great open waters. But they tried over and over again. While Wyville Thomson was taking a dredge at 1,225 fathoms, the device collapsed. On the second try in the same location the bag came up empty. The third time it caught on something, a rock perhaps, and was carried away. Before the trip was well begun, much of the *Challenger* equipment was strewn on the graveyard at the bottom of the ocean.

After the third failure to raise the dredge, young John Murray turned to Thomson and said, "Don't you ever lose your temper, sir?"

Thomson answered, "You can't expect success at once. It may take weeks for the men to get their sea legs and to learn to handle the gear."

"I guess you're right; I wish I had your patience, though."

Thomson knew that the few records he had managed to take between England and the Canary Islands were very inaccurate, so he threw them all away and decided that the real work would begin at Tenerife, the largest of the Canary Islands.

Although Thomson had nothing to show for the first couple of weeks' work, he did not ease up on his own schedule. If possible he charted a more detailed program for the ship than the Royal Society had outlined. Hadn't he been ordered to find out "everything about the sea?" This was to include both the biological and physical conditions of the oceans; record the temperatures both at the surface and in deep water; study the movements of the tides and the currents; chart the relation of barometric pressure to latitude; keep records of the chemical content of the water; and, most important, gather and classify the animals and plants at all levels of the ocean. (Fifty thousand meteorological observations were taken between December 1872 and December 1873.)

If these duties did not completely occupy the men's time, when they were on shore they were to study the geology of the land; investigate plants and animals (thirty directions were given the botanists alone); observe the types of government and the habits and customs of the people. Since the ship would, no doubt, stop at many places never before visited by Europeans, Wyville Thomson and his men were to be goodwill ambassadors for England.

Using Matthew Maury's *Wind and Tide Charts*, the *Challenger* was to follow an equally ambitious route. She was to study the oceans off Portugal, Spain, Azores, Cape Verde, Madeira, West Indies, Bermuda, South America, Straits of Magellan, Cape Horn, Australia, New Zealand, Indian Ocean, New Britain, Japan, "go as near as possible to the ice barrier," Aleutians, Vancouver Island, California. The *Challenger* would go back and forth across the Atlantic, the Pacific, the Indian, and the Antarctic oceans.

It makes one's head swim to read the itinerary and the program. So vast were the oceans, so long and tedious each investigation, so primitive the equipment that of course all the objectives couldn't be achieved. Even today, ninety years later, oceanographers with all manner of modern instruments and equipment are still trying to fit together the same puzzles that Wyville Thomson attempted to solve in four years. Although the expedition fell far short of its goal, it set the pattern for almost every oceanographic investigation from that day to this. Sir Ray Lancaster said, "Never did an expedition cost so little and produce such momentous results for human knowledge."

The rough stormy weather followed the *Challenger* even after passing Tenerife. The morale of the men was low, so Thomson decided to give them a rest in Lisbon. As the ship steamed into the Tagus River off Lisbon, a busyness and excitement gripped the men. How wonderful *terra firma* would feel after the rolling crowded ship.

"I'm going to stay at the Braganza Hotel which won't rock and roll. I need a good night's sleep," said Mr. Buchanan.

Thomson and the other scientists also needed a good night's sleep, so away they all went to the hotel. In the beautiful city of Lisbon for a few days the uncomfortable business of oceanography was forgotten. Night after night the officers and scientists danced and dined with the British Minister and his guests, and the sailors laughing and singing swarmed through the town. The King of Portugal, the first of many famous men to interest himself in the work of the *Challenger,* visited the ship.

This gaiety could not last long. Duty called Wyville Thomson back to the ship, so at six o'clock in the evening of January 12, the sunlighted, golden city redolent with the perfume of the orange and lemon harvest was left behind.

As if to make amends for the disappointments of earlier dredgings, beyond Lisbon at depths of 600 fathoms the sea gave up rich treasures, particularly delicate lacy sea fans a couple of feet in length. Attached to a thin wirelike axis, the broad fragile fans glowed with a soft pale lilac light as they waved back and forth with the slow current.

A few evenings later several seamen came running to Thomson. "The sea is all red as if it were on fire," they shouted. "What does it mean?"

Thomson rushed to the deck from his laboratory. Spread over the waters almost like a blanket were millions of tiny swimming snails called sea butterflies (pteropods) glittering in the moonlight. The attractive little creature gets its name from the foot that is modified into two bright red winglike appendages. As they move through the water, their bodies give off a perfect blaze of phosphorescent greens and blues. Thomson admitted it was a rare and beautiful sight.

Sea butterflies are not often seen alive in such masses as they appeared off Cape Vincent, but through the ages they have accumulated in immense numbers on the ocean floor as pteropod ooze. The sea butterflies led Thomson and Murray to study the soft clay deposits that everywhere cover the floor of the oceans. In dredges at depths of 525 fathoms or more in this area, the dredge bag was filled with the same type of material as was brought up with John Brooke's sounding device. For want of a better name John Murray called it "ooze." Everywhere was ooze, nothing but ooze.

Murray became so intrigued with the ooze he spent hours sieving it. Then late into the night he and Thomson sat huddled over their microscopes examining the dull deposit, which they found was composed almost entirely of the skeletons of tiny animals that had originally lived in the surface waters. This confirmed Professor Bailey's opinion that the ooze was formed through the ages when the remains of microscopic animals and plants fell through the miles of water to the ocean floor. The most widely distributed ooze is globigerina, the skeletons of a one-celled globe-shaped animal. This covers perhaps 60,000,000 square miles of sea bottom.

The investigation of globigerina ooze led Thomson and Murray to study other oozes. Some are composed of diatoms, infinitesimal plant forms; radiolarians, tiny one-celled animals; and sea butterflies, pteropods. Then there is the so-called red clay, a very ancient deposit found at 2,500 fathoms or more composed of disintegrated shells, ear bones of extinct whales, and teeth of long-gone sharks all cemented together by decomposed organic materials. Around many of the materials in the red clay are deposited iron and manganese spherules, no doubt gifts from outer space.

Thomson and Murray knew that eons ago the tiny plants and animals (now called plankton) that make up the oozes lived in the surface waters where they looked like dust particles suspended in the water. Although at the time of the *Challenger* expedition the existence of plankton was known, scientists had given so little study to this phase of the sea that the word "plankton," meaning "wanderer," had not been coined. Victor Hensen of Germany used the word for the first time in 1887 to characterize all the floating or drifting life in the sea. The *Challenger* scientists realized these tiny specks of life were a very important source of food to animals living in the sea; therefore during the three and a half years they collected four thousand species of plankton.

Believing these oozes also had much to tell about the history of life on this planet, Murray attempted to bore into the sediment that had become hardened, but succeeded in penetrating but two feet into the age-old deposits.

In the years since Thomson and Murray puzzled over the infinitesimal plankton, its study has become more and more important until today it is one of the principal fields of research for the marine biologist. The abundant life floating in the surface waters is now known to be the first link in the great food chain. In other words it forms the pastures of the sea and is the bread and butter of many marine animals, both large and small. Great monsters such as the Greenland whale as well as barnacles and clams live solely on plankton. And there is now the suggestion it may become important in the diet of man.

To collect living plankton forms from the surface waters, a net resembling a butterfly net is usually used. The net is a filtering cone with a collecting bottle at the end. At the other end it is attached to a metal ring by which the net is towed through the water. The net is most often some grade of silk bolting cloth with meshes so small the minute forms are caught and held within them.

For securing larger animals from the bottom, Thomson used the dredge. At depths of 800 to 1,000 fathoms, he found a great many animals from all the invertebrate groups. Often there were more starfish, sea urchins, crabs, and sponges clinging to the outside of the dredge than were in it. Noticing this, he recalled a ruse that Captain Carver of the *Porcupine* had played on the sailors who swabbed the decks.

Captain Carver had said, "Why not catch the spiny creatures by tying the rope mops the sailors use to the dredge?" This they did. At first the sailors were mystified as to what had become of their mops, but they willingly sacrificed them to the advancement of science. Remembering this incident, Thomson had provided the dredges on the *Challenger* with rope tails which picked up everything rough and movable in their paths and swept the ocean floor as clean as the sailors had swept the decks.

Dredging was a slow wearisome job, using almost a whole day to take a sampling of the ocean floor at a depth of 2,000 fathoms. It required an hour and a half for the dredge to reach the bottom. Then dragging it across the floor of the ocean with the ship rolling with the drift of the wind required several hours. Late in the afternoon the dredge rope would be placed on the drum and wound in, the process often requiring another three or four hours. Often the dredge would be so heavily weighted with specimens that the rope would break and the dredge and its contents lost.

To conserve time, whenever the ship was stopped while taking a dredge the physicists and chemists went into action too, noting temperatures, measuring speed of currents, analyzing the chemical content, or making other investigations of the waters. The sum of these operations was called taking a "station."

Murray, who was just as tireless and mentally curious as was Thomson, worked particularly on plankton, deposits on the sea bottom, and the formation of coral reefs. Under their combined efforts, the collections grew and grew until they almost crowded the men off the ship. These eager fishermen of the deep could not bear to throw away any of their hard-bought specimens. Who knew which tiny animal or plant might be a link in the endless chain of evidence in the fabulous story that the sea was telling?

Not only were the collections growing, but the men's understanding of the mysteries of the sea was growing even faster. Although they were still a long way from their goal of learning "everything about the sea," scarcely a day passed without some evidence of the synthesis of the many forces at work deep in the oceans. The pieces of the jigsaw puzzle began to mesh.

Early in the timetable of the expedition, Wyville Thomson found that at no depth were conditions in the water so severe that living things did not exist on the ocean floor, though he believed animals were neither so abundant, so large, nor so colorful at extreme depths as in shallow water. But contradicting this belief sea cucumbers and shrimps seemed to retain their normal sizes and colors even at depths of 3,000 fathoms. Likewise at 1,500 fathoms he dredged a wonderfully beautiful pink vaselike sponge which resembled spun glass. Small at the base, it flared out into a circular opening edged with an elaborate frill, while a lacelike lid closed the vase. A Venetian glass blower could not have fashioned a more exquisite objet d'art.

As Wyville Thomson became better acquainted with the life in the seas, he found the same animals over and over again in dredges at depths of 1,500 fathoms or more. Colorful sponges, jointed worms, dark red shrimps, long-legged crabs, fat sea cucumbers, and weird fish indicated to him that below a certain depth the water had a uniform temperature and a uniform fauna. Although in general this is true, it is now known that the distribution and the number of species is also dependent upon absorption of heat at different levels, variation of currents, and vertical motion. Strange as it may seem, the enormous pressure, utter darkness, differences in chemical and physical conditions of the water, and proportions of oxygen apparently have little effect upon life in the deep seas.

Thomson gave a great deal of attention to the eyes of the animals. In shallow water animals almost always had large eyes and keen sight. In deep water some had no eyes, while others had highly developed organs of sight. The eyes of many species from water 100 to 370 fathoms were already becoming useless. Eye stalks were present, but the animals apparently had no vision.

However, Wyville Thomson hesitated to draw conclusions about the relation of light to the eyes of deep sea animals, for no sooner did he do so than his theory was toppled. For instance, a Murida, a fish taken from 700 fathoms, had eyes of great delicacy. The best explanation he could give for this was that as the light rays in the water diminished, the vision of this animal became more acute by adapting to the fainter light of phosphorescence, the cold light given off by the animals themselves. But he felt safe in saying that as a general rule with increased depth there was a gradual decrease in vision. He believed too that many deep sea fish and shrimps compensate for the loss of sight by having long feelers with which they grope about.

During the early months of the cruise, the seamen almost fought to see the wriggling animals dumped from the trawl onto the deck.

"It's my turn, you keep out of it," they quarreled as they tried to grab a long-legged shrimp or a fiercely pinching crab. At first they were even interested in the gray or red ooze from the ocean floor. It wasn't long though before they became bored. "Just the same old stuff all the time, no matter which ocean it comes from."

After a time the most exciting game on shipboard was betting with gin and bitters as stakes on whether something new would be taken in the next dredge. Several rash boys wagered their grog for a week on their conviction that nothing new would be found in the next ten hauls.

It seemed strange that between Madeira and Bermuda the sea was very solitary. Day after day passed without a single creature —shark, porpoise, dolphin, or turtle—being visible. However, at the Azores there were several "firsts." Flying fish appeared for the first time, and bits of the wandering, deep seaweed, sargassum, floated by. Of course, Thomson had heard of sargassum and he was eager to see it because it defied the rule that seaweed must be attached to a solid object. Here, floating in the warm middle Atlantic hundreds of miles from land and in water several miles deep, were scattered great islets of olive-green feathery branched sargassum, the branches studded with air bladders to keep the weed floating. Between the branches of the weed were bright flashes of light given off by the small crustaceans and jellyfish as they glided through the water.

The branches of the sargassum often became a rest camp that afforded shelter to nomadic animals, large and small. One would expect these animals to be in great danger of being gobbled up by hungry fish and sharp-eyed birds, but they have developed such effective color camouflage and simulate the habits of their enemies so effectively they outwit them all.

When the *Challenger* had passed Trafalgar, the scene of Lord Nelson's great victory over Napoleon, Thomson and Captain Nares decided that everyone needed another rest. The next morning just at sunrise with the blue Mediterranean stretching away to the east without a ripple, the ship neared Gibraltar. Anchored near the great natural fortress was an endless line of British ships. As the *Challenger* hove into sight, the ships gave a booming salute to this lone wanderer of the seas. Though only a little past midwinter, the face of the Rock was garlanded with almond and aloe blossoms, while mauve bougainvillaea hung over verandas and fences. In high spirits all hands donned shore clothes and took off in launches to visit the "Guardian of the Mediterranean" and perhaps to catch sight of the monkeys that are said to assure its safety from attack.

By the end of the first year at sea, the crew and scientists on the *Challenger* were hardened to ugly weather and endless labor. Trawling, sounding, dredging, taking temperatures and water samples were all part of the job. The men had also become jacks-of-all-trades. They spliced cables, repaired dredges and microscopes, laughed at storms, and built more and more specimen cabinets.

For long hours every day of the week, Sunday, Monday, Tuesday, Saturday, the men patiently swept the floor of the oceans. Occasionally, Wyville Thomson confessed to John Murray that he was very tired. But in spite of his personal feelings, he is said never to have missed a dredge or trawl in the three and a half years that the expedition crossed and recrossed the ocean, sometimes in brilliant sunshine, sometimes in storms, sometimes in stifling heat, sometimes in paralyzing cold.

By this time Thomson probably knew more about the depths of the oceans than any man on earth, but one problem still bothered him. How could the animals withstand the terrific pressures of the water? The weight of the water was roughly a ton to the square inch at a depth of 1,000 fathoms, and two and a half tons at 2,500 fathoms. In contrast, the weight of the air at sea level was only fifteen pounds to the square inch.

"Could you run some experiments on the pressure?" Thomson asked Buchanan, the chemist. "It has me baffled."

In answer Buchanan filled a thick glass tube with air. This he hermetically sealed, wrapped the tube in flannel, placed it in a copper tube, and sent it down 2,000 fathoms. When it was drawn up, the copper tube was smashed beyond recognition, and the glass tube crushed to a powder fine as snow. Again and again Buchanan experimented. In the end he concluded the animals are not affected by the weight of the water because their tissues are permeated with liquid of the same density as the water; therefore the weight of the water has little effect upon them.

That this theory was correct was later demonstrated on the *Challenger* many times. Of the great numbers of fish taken from deep water only a few showed any effects of the changes in pressure. Buchanan concluded that it is only when animals are raised or lowered too rapidly for the tissues in their bodies to become adjusted to the changes in pressure that they suffer disastrous results. On several occasions when this happened the animals' eyes were forced out of their heads, the scales torn off their bodies, and their muscles were tense and swollen.

Wyville Thomson added much information about the seas, and he also pricked at least one bubble. Several scientists, including the great Thomas Huxley, believed that a gray gelatinous substance sometimes found in preserved specimens was a primitive protoplasmic slime, a complex substance considered the physical basis of life. It was a beautiful theory and explained many hitherto unanswerable problems neatly, but, unfortunately for its advocates, Buchanan chemically proved the supposedly magic substance (Bathybus, as it was called) was nothing more than sulphate of lime, precipitated when sea water is added to spirits of wine which had been used as a preservative. As a result of this experiment, Huxley publicly acknowledged his mistake.

The *Challenger* had now roamed the seas for three years. Wyville Thomson realized it was impossible to settle "once and for all everything about the seas." As one piece of the jigsaw puzzle fell into place, another even more difficult one demanded his attention. For instance, why did the great numbers of small animals living out at sea retire to deep water in the heat of the day and come to the surface in the cool of the evening? From the days of the *Challenger* until today, marine scientists have tried to explain this vertical migration of the animals. In his 1956 book *The Open Sea,* Sir Alister Hardy says, "It [the vertical migration] is still the number one plankton problem," and it is an indication of the complexity of oceanographic problems and the time involved in their solution.

After long periods of confinement on the ship, the endless routine of trawling became unbearable to the men. Even Robert, the parrot, got tired of the everlasting talk of dredging. This veteran of the *Challenger*, his leg crippled, his feathers ruffled, constantly called from his perch on the hatrack, "What, Dr. Thomson, Fellow Royal Society, 2,000 fathoms and no bottom."

To relieve the monotony, the captain occasionally took the *Challenger* into some far-flung outpost of the world. The ship visited Christmas Island and Kerguelen Land in the Indian Ocean; St. Paul's Rocks, Tristan de Cunha, Inaccessible in the Atlantic, and dozens of other islands.

Although tiny St. Paul's Rocks, lying close to the equator, are so barren not a plant, not even a lichen, grows upon them, birds in such numbers breed upon the Rocks that they are almost pure white from the droppings. (Darwin had commented on the great flocks of birds on these rocks.) The rocks are so steep that to land upon them the men had to spring from the skiffs and scramble onto the Rocks when the boat was on top of a wave. Inaccessible Island was inhabited by thousands of penguins busily engaged in building their rookeries and by two ship-wrecked German brothers who entertained the Englishmen with strange stories of their experiences. To the Germans' great delight, the *Challenger* rescued them from their penguin companions.

On these lonely islands Henry Moseley made endless notes on the life of the albatross, giant snails, sea elephants, and whales, and wrote a fascinating description of the habits of the penguin. He made studies of the natives of New Hebrides, New Guinea, Admiralty Islands, Tonga, Fiji, and all the others. He investigated everything. He met and talked to the natives, often only by signs and gestures. He inquired into the influence of the missionaries and western trade routes. He searched out the original handicrafts of the people, which he saw were fast disappearing. He knew that once these native arts were gone they would never be recovered and there would be a gap in the records of mankind. He sketched, photographed, and collected all sorts of materials, and it may well be that today these records and collections are among the most important contributions of the expedition. It was said of Henry Moseley that you had only to put him down on a hillside with a piece of string and an old nail, and in an hour or two he would have discovered some natural object of surprising interest.

In February 1875 the *Challenger* crossed the Antarctic Circle, the first steam vessel to do so, where for weeks she carried on the almost impossible task of trawling among the forest of icebergs. Often on a cold night rang out the call, "All hands on board," as the ship came near colliding with a berg that loomed through the falling snow.

In good weather in this area, everyone dredged, trawled, and took water temperatures almost around the clock. The work became so gruelling the men longed for gales to come when the ship would be weatherbound and the endless trawling among the bergs would have to stop. When this happened, with a sigh of relief they crawled into their bunks indifferent to the wind lashing the ship and the fog closing in around them. During these anxious days the captain and Thomson peered anxiously from the pilothouse windows.

While creeping between the islands toward the Straits of Magellan, sounding and trawling almost every day, the dredge brought up a splendid series of South American animals from 50 to 400 fathoms. At Stanley Harbor, the seat of government of the Falkland Islands Dependencies (about a hundred in number), which since 1831 has been under the British flag, the *Challenger* stopped for several days. The climate in the islands was miserable—cold, rainy, and foggy. The sun rarely shone, but valuable herds of sheep and cattle provided a stable industry for the inhabitants.

As was their custom, upon the arrival of the ship at inhabited islands, the captain and Wyville Thomson called upon the Governor, Colonel D'Arcy, who was very cordial. As a result of this call, Mr. Moseley was asked to inspect some beds of graphite and seams of coal which the governor hoped were workable. However, they proved to be of no value commercially.

Thomson was particularly delighted to meet a bishop stationed in these almost barbaric islands, "Not a bishop blunt of speech and careless of externals, as so hard a working missionary among the Fuegians and Patagonians might well afford to be, but a bishop gracious in manner and perfect in attire, who would have seemed more in harmony with the surroundings in St. James or Windsor." To keep in touch with his diocese, which included the whole southern coast of South America, this zealous and active man traveled in a little missionary schooner. Everywhere he was greatly beloved. His parishioners, laden with gifts, greeted his arrival with joy.

Thomson could not help but feel that his great influence was due to the care with which he maintained the culture and refinement of a gentleman and the dignity of the church he served.

It was now January 1876. The *Challenger* by following Matthew Maury's *Wind and Current Charts* had without accident crossed the equator six times. She had sailed from the Arctic to the Antarctic, and had criss-crossed from Australia and the Indian Ocean to the Mediterranean. Most of the lands Thomson had hoped to see had been visited and most of the seas had been dredged. The collecting cases were bursting with specimens and the files with records. So the *Challenger* turned homeward in a northerly course on the central ridge of the Atlantic toward Ascension, a curious little volcanic island which was in commission as one of Her Majesty's ships, for everyone on the island was more or less connected with the service. On shore, discipline was as rigid as was a ship in a foreign station.

As if to remind the men of the stormy cold days of the early part of the expedition, the northwest winds began to blow. To escape the wind's fury, the *Challenger* finally hove into Vigo in southwest Spain to wait out the storm and to give the men a run on shore. Moored in the bay at Vigo was the British Channel Fleet. As soon as the *Defense* recognized the *Challenger*, the band struck up "Home, Sweet Home." This was too much to bear. Tears sprang to the eyes of the men who had been away so long and this tune strained their emotions far more than savages and icebergs had done.

On the homeward journey everyone relaxed somewhat. To while away the time Henry Moseley added copious notes to his diary. Jokingly he recounted that when the ship left England it had been "inhabited by men, dogs, and livestock needed for food, but soon many other 'boarders' had moved in. Small red ants made trails up the legs of tables; cockroaches, clothes moths, house flies, crickets and centipedes took up their abodes with the men. At Bermuda rats invaded the ship." One night when the men were playing cards, the assistant paymaster suddenly gave a yell and clutched at his pants as a rat ran up his leg. Two large tortoises, spiders, a fur seal and a young goat were added to the cargo. The talkative parrot continued to bait Wyville Thomson about the incessant dredging. Moseley added that the strange boarders did not bother the men, none of which were stranger than those they were collecting from the bottom of the sea.

By this time Henry Moseley had been at sea so long, his six-by-six cabin had become home. He almost regretted leaving it. On shipboard one escapes so many distractions of shore life, he said.

In a more serious vein, Wyville Thomson reviewed the work of the expedition. In three and a half years the ship had traveled 69,000 miles and had established 362 observation stations. (At each station a dozen or more tests were made.) Out of the 243 men who had left England, sixty-one had deserted; at least one had been lost overboard; Dr. von Willemoes Suhm had died of erysipelas; Captain Nares had been transferred to a ship bound for the Arctic and had been replaced by Captain Frank Thomson. Of course there had been a few minor accidents. But most remarkable was the good feeling that existed on board, especially between the ship's crew and the scientists.

Recalling the endless routine of the work, Dr. Thomson tried to see the overall pattern of the expedition. He felt he could truthfully say, "Mission accomplished."

Of course, until the materials were carefully examined, it was impossible to say what scientific findings the *Challenger* had made. As yet very little had been done on the chemical analyses; natural history specimens were still locked in their cases.

But Thomson's brain was crammed with a thousand conclusions concerning the sea. For instance, he had been deeply impressed with the uniform way in which the water deepened in all the seas. After passing a narrow, shallow belt (the continental shelf, about 600 feet) the water deepens rapidly to 2,000 to 2,500 fathoms; then it deepens slowly, until at one spot the Atlantic reaches a depth of 3,875 fathoms, while the Pacific is twice that depth at its deepest point. (The Challenger Deep had not yet been discovered.)

The water, too, in all the seas is warmest at the surface. It cools rapidly down to 100 fathoms, then loses its heat slowly to depths of 500 to 600 fathoms, while below this depth it changes little in temperature to the bottom where it maintains a nearly uniform temperature of 29° to 34° F. This in turn explains the similarity everywhere of fauna near the ocean floors. Because of their dependence upon sunlight, no plants live below 100 fathoms.

There was no question that the expedition had fulfilled the original objective of the trip, by making a survey of the animals that live in the ocean, as the hundreds of cases of specimens proved. Perhaps the most important thing the expedition revealed was that the sea is a great complex of conditions so intricately interwoven it would be centuries before men fully understood them all. As Matthew Maury had said, the sea is an amazing and beautiful combination of the works of the "First Great Thought."

After leaving Vigo, driven by a strong wind the *Challenger* flew up the Bay of Biscay as if she were as eager to get home as were the men. As the ship sped toward the English Channel, the men scanned the horizon endlessly, hoping for the first glimpse of their beloved England. On the evening of May 21, 1876, the *Challenger* dropped anchor in seven fathoms of water at Spithead. Cheers were deafening and hats were flung into the air. The men went wild as they embraced their wives and marveled at the growth of their children.

The homecoming was joyous, but for the scientists perhaps the hardest work was still ahead of them. Wyville Thomson was plunged into endless conferences, lectures, and social engagements, and was awarded the Gold Medal of the Royal Society. Mr. Wyville Thomson became Sir Wyville. He was also appointed Director of the Challenger Expedition Commission, the purpose of which was to see to the distribution and detailed study of the vast collections and the publication of results.

For this work an office was set up in Edinburgh. So great was the renown of the Expedition and the scientists and so unique and immense the collections that scholars from all parts of the world flocked to Edinburgh to see them. Sir Wyville realized that specialists in the various branches of science from many countries would be needed to adequately describe the tens of thousands of plants and animals that had been so carefully collected and labeled. And so began perhaps the greatest pooling of scientific knowledge on a common project that scientists had ever undertaken.

In addition to carrying out the tremendous load of work heaped upon him, Sir Wyville found time to publish in 1877 a two volume summary of the cruise entitled, *Voyage of the Challenger, the Atlantic,* a fascinating work full of interesting comment upon the many phases of the voyage. A companion volume, *The Pacific,* was to have followed, but it was never finished.

Soon after the publication of the first volume of the book, Sir Wyville suffered an attack of paralysis. However, he continued to work whenever he was able. His most notable expedition of this time was the investigation of a high submarine ridge in the Faroe Channel. On one side of the ridge were warm water animals and on the other cold water forms. Because of his health he was unable to complete the study of this problem, but in 1882 John Murray learned that this ridge formed a temperature barrier with entirely different animals on either side. Thomson soon suffered other attacks until he had to give up his work entirely. He died in 1882 at the age of fifty-two, his life no doubt shortened by the exposure and the rigors of the *Challenger* Expedition.

Just twenty years after the *Challenger* had returned to England, John Murray, now Sir John, who had been appointed to succeed Sir Wyville as Director of the Challenger Expedition Commission, deposited in the British Museum the last of the fifty volumes describing the materials collected on the Expedition. Each volume was most carefully edited and a number of them beautifully illustrated. Not without reason are they called "The Holy Writ of Deep Sea Oceanography."

Never had an expedition gained so much lasting fame as did the *Challenger*. This fame was due in large part to the care with which the plants and animals had been collected and the results published. In fact the *Challenger* is said to have brought back more information about the seas than had been learned in the previous eighteen hundred years.

Nor does her glory diminish with the years. Almost every biologist who visits England makes a pilgrimage to the British Museum to see this famous set of books and to pay homage to the dedicated men who sailed on the *Challenger*. And no student of science today can read far without meeting references to this pioneering expedition.

❖   ❖   ❖

The men on the *Challenger* did not learn "everything about the sea," but they pointed the way to hundreds of investigations of the waters that surround and dominate our planet. Inspired by the work done by the men on the *Challenger* and eager to extend their researches, Alexander Agassiz devoted his life and his wealth to further investigations of far-flung areas of the seas.

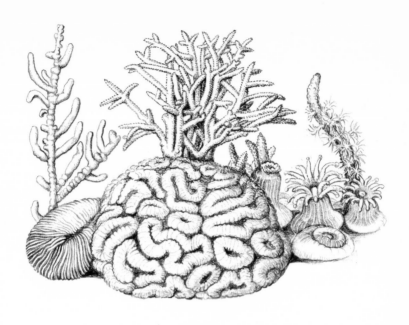

4

Alexander Agassiz —
The Blake *and the* Albatross

And I have loved thee, Ocean!

Thirteen-year-old Alexander Agassiz was leaving Switzerland for the United States to join his famous father, Louis Agassiz. Alexander had heard that America was the land of the free where everyone could do as he pleased. One morning after two hours of practice on his violin he decided to celebrate the freedom which would soon be his by jumping on his violin, which he hated, breaking it into a hundred pieces.

The elder Agassiz was a well-known Swiss scientist who was reputed to know "every fish that swims in the sea, every bird that flies over our heads, every insect that crawls in the grass, and every plant that grows on the mountain sides." He also knew "almost everything" about fossil fish and glaciers, but he was not satisfied with knowing "almost everything" about the ice age, so in 1845, to learn more about glacial action, to secure money to publish his researches, and perhaps to make influential friends, he left his wife and children in Switzerland and came to the United States.

In addition to learning about glaciers, Louis Agassiz, a sociable, charming man and a brilliant teacher, learned many things about the United States and came to love this new country. Almost at once he made friends with John Lowell, trustee and director of the Lowell Institute in Boston. Soon he was giving lectures at the Institute, was a Professor of Natural Science at Harvard, and was going to dinner parties.

When his wife died of tuberculosis in 1848, he began planning to bring his children, Alexander, Pauline, and Ida, to America. Alexander arrived about a year after his mother's death and his father soon married Elizabeth Cary, an intelligent, charming woman from a well-known Boston family. On her wedding day she said to Alexander, "My dear, I am now your mother. May we love one another." With these words the new Mrs. Agassiz went straight to young Alexander's heart where she stayed all the rest of her long life —his mother, his devoted friend, and his companion. At once she sent for Alexander's sisters, Pauline and Ida, who were equally fond of their new mother.

To the charming home that Louis and Elizabeth Agassiz established on Quincy Street in Cambridge came many distinguished men of Harvard. Such men as Asa Gray, Jeffries Wyman, Henry Wadsworth Longfellow, James Russell Lowell, and dozens of others were at home there, and the talk that swirled around the handsome, shy Swiss boy was a liberal education, and Alexander drank it all in.

Although Alexander was handicapped at first by knowing no English, he could chatter fluently in French and German. And he managed to communicate with the boys in Cambridge High School through his proficiency in Latin. Nevertheless in a few months Alexander was chattering in English as glibly as he had done in German and French. His new freedom also included wandering in the woods to collect insects, snakes, and butterflies of which he made handsome collections.

Alexander entered Harvard at fifteen and a half where his well-trained mind and his ability to concentrate made him the envy and the despair of the average easygoing undergraduate. Yet he was no grind. Very soon he was answering to the name "Swiss," was playing leading roles in University theatricals, making posters for the Hasty Pudding Club, swinging an enormous pair of Indian clubs, and serving as bow on the Harvard crew, a sport he followed closely all his life.

In spite of his interest in dramatics and athletics, Alexander left the intangibles, such as philosophy, literature, and music to others, concentrating upon chemistry, geology, mathematics, and zoology, his favorite study. He graduated from Harvard in 1855.

While still a student at Harvard Alexander taught classes in his mother's select school for girls. Louis Agassiz had never known the value of a dollar, letting money slip through his fingers like water. For this reason it was necessary for Mrs. Agassiz to supplement the family budget. In her school was a beautiful girl named Anna Russell with whom Alexander fell madly in love.

Warned by his father's example of the difficulties of making enough money as a naturalist to marry and support a family, Alexander thought it would be quicker and easier to get rich as an engineer than as a naturalist, so he enrolled in the Lowell Scientific School, from which he graduated in mining engineering *magna cum laude*. With his engineering degree secured, he kissed his sweetheart a sad goodbye, and set off for San Francisco to join the Coast Survey as a surveyor's aide on the *Fauntleroy*, which was to chart the Gulf of Georgia, the boundary between British Columbia and the United States.

Since the *Fauntleroy* was delayed in reaching San Francisco, Alexander, to while away the time until the ship arrived, went to Crescent City by coast steamer, where he tramped the seashore gathering all sorts of strange animals and making sketches and notes on them which he sent to his father at the Harvard Museum. In the fall when the fogs became so dense in the Strait of Juan de Fuca that the men could no longer survey, the *Fauntleroy* was again delayed in returning them to San Francisco. During this enforced idleness Alexander made a study of the jellyfish and collected a number of perch.

After a summer in the Coast Survey and a three-month stay in Panama, Alexander decided that government service offered no more opportunity of making quick money than did the teaching of natural science, and certainly being a naturalist was infinitely more interesting and challenging. Having made this decision, Alexander resigned from his Coast Survey position and straight as a homing pigeon hurried back to his sweetheart and his father's museum, which ever afterward remained his headquarters. Alexander was sure no work could be more satisfying than was that of his father and he was happy to follow in his footsteps. Almost immediately he was appointed agent for the newly established Harvard Museum of Comparative Zoology at a salary of $1,500 a year. Alexander married Anna Russell in 1860 and the newlyweds moved into the Quincy Street house with his father and stepmother. He was happy and rejoiced in his work; his gaiety and charm made him welcome everywhere. He took another degree in zoology.

All went well at the museum until 1861 when most of the employees went off to the Civil War with the Union army. Agassiz, who had only recently become an American citizen, decided to stay at home and keep the Museum from going to pieces. His decision not to take sides was also partly motivated by loyalty to Southern friends who had given him very happy times when he had accompanied his father to South Carolina on a lecture tour when he first came to the United States.

Although he was head over heels in the affairs of the museum, Alexander found time during the war years to do his first original research, working on the mechanical principles involved in the flight of certain insects. Some years earlier, Mrs. Louis Agassiz's father had given his daughter and her husband a summer home on the seashore at Nahant, Massachusetts. This they shared with Alexander and his young wife. In the bay back of the house was a dory and near the beach was a shed which Alexander and his father made into a laboratory equipped with microscopes and glass containers. The beachcombing on the West Coast had introduced Alex to marine animals. Now the dory and the laboratory added their spell and he was committed to marine biology for life. From this primitive laboratory Alex wrote a series of papers on the embryology of sea urchins and starfish. In 1861 he and his stepmother published *Seashore Studies in Natural History* and a few years later *Marine Animals of Massachusetts Bay,* both accurate and charming studies.

Charles Darwin had published his *Origin of Species* in 1859. At once scientists as well as laymen engaged in violent discussions on the subject of evolution, splitting the world into two hostile camps. Louis Agassiz was bitterly opposed to Darwin's theory, fighting it to the end of his life. Alexander did not agree with Darwin, but he was willing to follow the discussions, saying he would study them "whithersoever they may lead, but would be satisfied with no theory, no wonderful panaceas until I see something more substantial to uphold them than I can discern at present in the Darwinian theory."

Alexander's $1,500 salary was now, with a wife and three small sons to support, very inadequate. He had been haunted by the lack of money ever since the days when his father had left his family behind in Switzerland and gone off to America. His mother was so ill that this mite of a boy had taken charge of the pathetic little household, keeping the small accounts, marketing, and running errands.

Now, to support his own family comfortably, Alexander once more had to look around for a better paying job. After searching in vain for several weeks, he was offered the presidency of some mines in Pennsylvania, for which his degree in mining engineering had prepared him. He took the job, but he soon found these mines offered almost no possibility of growth.

In 1868 he was asked to take charge of the Calumet and Hecla copper mines in northern Michigan. Although they were in a run-down condition, Alexander saw great possibilities in them. He took a leave of absence from the museum, begged and borrowed money from his relatives to buy a large block of stock in the mines, and worked day and night to get them on their feet. The laziness of the miners infuriated Alexander, but at the end of two years the mines were producing considerable copper. Alexander, although of slight build, had always been remarkably powerful and active, but in making the mines pay he seriously injured his health. To recuperate, he went back to the museum, but he retained the presidency of the mines.

Realizing the young man had broken his health in the mines, in 1871 James Lawrence, a close friend, gave Alexander and his family a trip to Europe. After a leisurely visit with relatives in Switzerland, he wandered far and wide meeting the great scientists of the day. In England he came to know the biologists Owen, Wallace, Huxley, and Darwin. In Belfast Wyville Thomson told him that on the *Porcupine* he had dredged animals off the bottom of the sea at the unbelievable depth of 2,500 fathoms, and that he believed that the great scientific advances of the future lay in oceanography. With this introduction Agassiz and Thomson became fast friends, keeping up a lively correspondence until Thomson's death.

Although Alexander did not completely regain the robust strength of his youth, he returned from Europe much improved in health and deeply inspired by the work that these scientists were doing in the new field of oceanography. With renewed enthusiasm he began to revise his studies on the sea urchins and the starfish. When the studies were finished in 1872, Alexander Agassiz was hailed as the greatest authority in the world on this interesting group of animals.

Louis Agassiz, after a number of years as a teacher, research worker, traveler, museum director, and social lion, died in 1873. Eight days later a much greater sorrow came to Alexander when his young wife, Anna, died of pneumonia, the attack probably brought on through overwork and exposure while caring for her father-in-law. Alexander was heartbroken. He could not reconcile himself to the death of his loved one. But with his usual courage, he faced his sorrow squarely. In a letter to Thomas Huxley, he said, "How gladly I would exchange all I have for what I have lost, but I will not burden you with my sorrow." At that time Alexander Agassiz evolved a philosophy of life which he ever afterward followed: "To live our lives as they have been made for us, and live in hope, do the best we can, work hard, and have as many interests as possible in what is going on around us." If ever a man lived by his own creed, it was Alexander Agassiz. Yet from this time on he developed a reserve, a sort of inner life in which he really lived, and it was only to his intimate friends that his old gaiety showed itself.

After his wife's death, Alexander and his three young sons moved back to his father's house on Quincy Street and lived very happily with his stepmother, who brought up the boys as fondly as if they were her own children. With the dearest tie of his life broken, Alexander filled his time and his mind by plunging deeper and deeper into the study of oceanography. In 1876 when the *Challenger* returned from her historic trip, he went to Edinburgh to help Wyville Thomson sort out the collections and to distribute them to specialists for identification and classification, doing a large part of the research and making the drawings of the starfish and sea urchins himself.

Agassiz was so caught up in the enthusiasm which the success of the *Challenger* Expedition had aroused on both sides of the Atlantic that then and there he swore he would become a member of an oceanographic expedition at the very first opportunity. His friends agreed his native abilities as well as his training made him an ideal leader in investigations of the sea. He was both a scholar and a man of action. He had a wide knowledge of marine zoology; he had training in engineering; he knew how to construct and repair equipment; and he knew how to handle men.

His first real opportunity to go on an expedition came in 1877 when the director of the United States Coast Survey asked him to take charge of a series of dredging cruises on the 350-ton schooner *Blake.* As soon as he saw the ship, Agassiz realized a number of changes were necessary before it would be satisfactory for deep sea work. The first thing he did was to substitute steel rope for hemp in dredging, coiling 18,000 feet on reels which took up far less space than the bulky hemp had done. He also changed the arrangement of the drums and other apparatus used in hoisting. He used flat frames on the dredges instead of rectangular ones, and redesigned the trawl without the digging and scraping edge it had formerly had and made it considerably larger, so that it worked equally well on whichever side it fell into the water.

No doubt the most important change was in John Brooke's device for deep sounding. The great advantage of the wire cable over hemp was that the sounder could be lowered by friction brakes and hoisted up with a donkey engine in much less time than formerly, and the wire had a high breaking strain of 8,600 pounds. The new sounder measured the water's depth so easily that Agassiz hoped that soon all passenger steamers would have devices for measuring the depth of the water to prevent their running aground.

Best of all, the improved sounding methods saved much time. On the *Challenger* it had taken the best part of a day to complete one dredge at 1,500 fathoms. On the *Blake* a dredge of 805 fathoms was at the bottom in twenty-five minutes and in one hour and twenty-three minutes it was back on deck. On the first trip of the *Blake* only 200 feet of cable were lost. With such a smoothly operating sounder, Agassiz investigated the deep seas endlessly. During his lifetime he traveled over 100,000 miles in his investigations of the seas.

When Agassiz dedicated his life to the study of the sea, he probably did not realize that he became violently seasick the minute he set foot on board. This malady did not daunt him in the least, for he was always out of his bunk at five o'clock in the morning letting down the dredge, then awaiting the treasures from the deep which would be hidden among the cold, slimy materials which the dredge would bring up. One day, while examining the contents of the dredge, Agassiz was struck with a sudden, severe attack of nausea. (This was before the days of dramamine.) Having tried every conventional remedy for mal de mer without success, his shipmates fed him pineaple, fried bananas, and sauerkraut. "It seems a queer combination but it worked admirably and kept me well alive," Agassiz admitted.

Equipped with the modern dredging devices, the *Blake* worked the waters around Cuba, the Yucatan Banks, Key West, and the Tortugas, ending the cruise at New Orleans. Very soon after starting out, Agassiz discovered the fauna on the Yucatan Banks were almost identical with those of Florida. In the Caribbean, Agassiz dredged many animals identical with those taken by the *Challenger* from many parts of the world. Although by this time scientists were familiar with globigerina ooze, they had not often seen the animals alive. However, one clear evening, much to the amazement of everyone, the surface of the water was covered with live globigerinae (minute one-celled globelike animals), the bright red nucleus of the cell coloring the whole area a vivid scarlet. As he gathered these microscopic bits of life in a fine silk net, Agassiz wondered how many years or centuries it would take for these tiny animals to be compressed into ooze.

In all his work Agassiz gave great attention to detail, but like Matthew Maury he never forgot that details were but cogs in the great balance wheel of the sea or tiny pieces in the jigsaw puzzle. The animals and plants, the movements of the currents and the tides, the contours of the ocean floor, the formation of sediment he believed were but part of the whole story of the sea in which all the parts work together in perfect harmony.

Within a year after the first voyage of the *Blake*, Agassiz was back on the ship for another cruise with many of the same officers and men. He worked in the same general area as on the earlier survey. One day, while sitting on the deck examining the contents of the dredge, his back scorching, his tongue parched, his hands freezing, a thought popped into his mind. Why couldn't the cold water be used as a refrigerator? "We need a cold drink," he suggested to his co-workers. Putting his thought into action, he sent a bottle of champagne down to a depth of 2,400 fathoms. When the bottle was brought back on deck an hour later, it was cold all right, but, sad to say, it was filled with bitter salty water, the great pressure of the water having forced out the cork. "All that good champagne wasted on the fishes," Agassiz lamented.

By the end of the season, Agassiz had occupied two hundred stations and made two hundred and thirty hauls from depths of 100 to 2,412 fathoms. The richest hauls came from 200 to 2,000 fathoms, while the greatest number of species came from 300 to 1,000 fathoms. In some places there were such myriads of animals Agassiz said that the bottom must have been paved with brittle and basket stars, while the shallows must have been covered with starfish and sea urchins. The collections were so large that, added to those of the previous year, his material was almost as complete as was the *Challenger's*. With the enthusiasm of a boy trading marbles with a friend, Agassiz wrote to Wyville Thomson to ask if he would like some of his specimens. "In one haul," Agassiz told Thomson, "124 rare sea lilies were brought up. I thought I would jump overboard when the tangles came up with them."

Between cruises Agassiz went back to the Harvard Museum where he directed the classification of the materials, arranged for their shipment to Edinburgh, attended to the innumerable tasks of the Museum, and oversaw the operation of the mines of which he was still president. During these sojourns in Boston, Agassiz rode horseback, tramped the woods, and attended dinner parties with old friends, where for a short time he put away his reserve and kept the guests in gales of laughter with fascinating stories and anecdotes.

In the summer of 1880 Agassiz was off on a third cruise on the *Blake*. The object of this journey was to sound the depths of the Gulf Stream, running a series of lines of dredges from the eastern edge of George's Shoal to Charleston, South Carolina, a part of the Atlantic untouched by the *Challenger* Expedition. Animal life in this area was very scanty. At first Agassiz could not explain it, but finally he decided it was due in part to the gradual slope of the continental shelf toward deep water, and in part to the swift current of the Gulf Stream that carried everything along its course off the bottom.

But the most exciting discovery was that the materials in the dredge indicated that at one time the Caribbean Sea was an arm of the Pacific Ocean or at least closely connected with it. This helped to explain, Agassiz decided, why the fauna of the West Indies was more like that of Central and South America than of the southern part of the United States and why the deep sea fauna on both sides of the Isthmus of Panama had a closer relationship to each other than do those of the Caribbean to the deep sea forms of the Atlantic. (The general belief today is that in ages past North and South America were completely separated.)

Agassiz had expected to find in the deep seas extinct geological or fossil forms which would be very different from present-day species. He did not find this to be the case, however. There were almost no extinct forms. Apparently, through thousands of years as the animals descended from the shores and other shallow regions, they gradually became adjusted to conditions of the deep. Both Wyville Thomson and Alexander Agassiz found that in water deeper than 500 fathoms in any part of the world temperatures, darkness, food supplies, and animals varied very little or were perfectly uniform. If this is so, once animals have become acclimated to certain zones, they can live and spread anywhere. It also explained why deep sea fauna includes species similar to those in shallow water in both warm and cold latitudes.

Judging by the evidence of his dredges, Agassiz pictured the sea bottom above the continental shelf (a depth of 600 feet) as carpeted with brilliantly colored animals. (Pictures taken by the aqualungers have shown this to be true.) Below this sunlighted area the animals gradually became darker and more scarce. Agassiz compares this continually decreasing life in the sea as depth increases to ascending a high mountain where the vegetation gradually becomes scanty and poor. He says, "It requires but little imagination to notice contrasts as we pass from shallow water regions of the sea full of sunlight and movement and teeming with animal and plant life to the dimly lighted but richly populated Continental zone, and further to imagine the gradual decrease of this Continental zone as it fades into the calm, cold, dark and nearly deserted abyssal regions of the oceanic floor at distances far from the continents."

He continues, "In contrast to the brilliantly colored animals of the shallow water, the deep sea floor is a monotony only relieved by dead carcasses of animals which find their way from the surface to the bottom and which supply the principal food for the scanty fauna found living there."

It was a lucky day for oceanography when Alexander Agassiz took a degree in engineering, for he did much to improve oceanographic equipment, which was one of the greatest needs of the early marine scientists. Through his skill in improving techniques and conditions of dredging and towing, on the third cruise of the *Blake* he was able to do as much work in eighteen days as he had done in three months on the first cruise.

On the third cruise Agassiz experimented with an ingenious tow net for sampling a column of water from any height or any depth, in other words, to isolate the animals that live and move and have their being at different levels between the upper 100 fathoms, and those living on or near the bottom. He hoped to be able to determine the exact depth from which a given sample of water or a given animal was taken. However, he was unable to do this. Agassiz therefore concluded, as Wyville Thomson had done, that between the animals living near the surface and those inhabiting the bottom there was a vast belt of water where practically no life existed. In later years he admitted the upper zone was perhaps thicker than he had at first thought. (We now know the water is inhabited at all depths.)

Through Agassiz's friendship with Wyville Thomson, the collections from the first two cruises of the *Blake* were sent to the same specialists for identification as had studied the *Challenger* materials. Their reports were published by the Harvard Museum. The specimens from the third cruise were given by the United States Fish Commission to the naturalists along the Atlantic seaboard.

During the 1880's in an attempt to relieve circulatory troubles which he had suffered ever since his hard work in the mines, Agassiz made many journeys to warmer climates, combining pleasure and much hard work. During these years he planned a five-year program for the Calumet mines which by this time had reached huge proportions: 930 tons of ore a day were being extracted from the earth. From 1869 to 1909 they paid its stockholders $108,850,000 in dividends. The income from the mines had solved all of Alexander's financial worries. He had become a very wealthy man, sponsoring scientific expeditions to far places of the world, helping ambitious students to do advanced work, and giving at least $1,500,000 to the Harvard Museum. He also wrote fifty-nine articles and books on his oceanographic researches, and collected degrees and honors from universities at home and abroad. One honor he particularly prized was his election as a foreign member to the Royal Society of London. Of this he wrote, "Although I have little ambition, yet I have a very soft spot in my heart for the praise of my peers."

No matter how far he traveled during the winters, Agassiz returned each summer to Newport, Rhode Island, where for twenty-five years (until 1898) he directed a small laboratory for graduate students. Here to the end of his life he carried on his own studies on the life histories of jellyfish, sea anemones, and corals, with an occasional experiment on their protective colorations.

Toward the end of the decade, Agassiz eagerly accepted the invitation of the United States Fish Commission to take charge of a deep sea expedition on the Pacific side of Panama on the *Albatross*, a beautiful modern ship 234 feet long with a beam 27 feet and six inches, and equipped with a laboratory and most modern instruments for ocean study.

His son Maxmillian now accompanied Agassiz on his expeditions. Ever since his first cruise to the Caribbean in 1880, Alexander had wanted to explore the waters on the Pacific side of the Panama Canal. He believed a comparison of the deep sea fauna on the two sides of the isthmus would show the animal evolution that had taken place in the geological periods since the continents had been joined together.

Writing to Thomas Huxley about the proposed cruise, Agassiz said, "I have always dreamed of dredging and sounding in the Pacific. My mouth waters at all the problems to be solved." Out of his own pocket Agassiz furnished the coal for the *Albatross*, paid for the oceanographic equipment, and guaranteed part of the running expenses. In return he was to get his choice of the collections.

Agassiz joined the *Albatross* after it had traveled down the east coast of North and South America, around Cape Horn, and made its way up the western coast of South America. He came aboard at Panama, accompanying the ship to Ecuador and to the Galapagos Islands. In describing the journey from Ecuador to the Galapagos to the Director of the United States Fish Commission, Agassiz tells of the monotony, dreariness, and desolation of the ocean depths in this part of the world, and of the grueling work on a research vessel.

At five o'clock each morning the seamen who were to operate the dredge were hustled from their bunks to begin their long day's work. After swallowing a makeshift breakfast, they took a sounding to learn the ocean's depth, then a bottom sample of ooze was raised.

This having been carefully deposited in the laboratory for later examination, the great dredge boom was swung over the side of the ship and the trawl lowered. The ship "lay to" while three or four miles of wire were paid out. When the cable reached the bottom, the vessel steamed slowly ahead dragging the dredge across the ocean floor to pick up anything that happened to be in its path.

While this was going on, Agassiz kept a close watch on the dredge dial to be sure the strain on the cable was not so great as to break it. He didn't want to run the risk of losing the dredge and the specimens. When he assumed the trawl was full, the vessel was again stopped and the long process of winding in the endless line began.

Having reached the surface, the dredge was swung toward the ship and the animals that it contained were dumped onto the deck, the materials dripping with ice cold water. Agassiz peered at each fresh gift from the sea as though it were a precious treasure. A further sorting and preserving of the material went on in the laboratory, where the most delicate forms were sketched on the spot. These were placed in small vials for safekeeping, while the larger ones were put in casks with preserving fluids.

Not satisfied with working from dawn to dark, on clear moonlit nights the men fished the plankton organisms by attracting them toward the surface with electric lights. As they swam toward the lights, they were collected in fine silk nets, then placed in glass bottles to await later microscopic examination.

While the *Albatross* was anchored on the bleak, barren Galapagos Islands, Agassiz took some time off from his oceanographic work to hunt for huge turtles, which were said to live there. These great animals, he believed, would lend a realistic touch to the Pacific exhibit in the Harvard Museum. But his only reward after a full day of turtle hunting was a painful sunburn.

Between Inaccessible Island and Acapulco, Mexico, he hoped to dredge many animals not hitherto found because it was a region the *Challenger* had not investigated, but time after time the dredge came up with only a handful of materials or else the net was torn to shreds by the rocks below. Discouraging as this was, Agassiz was well satisfied with the great variety of materials he had procured earlier on the trip. He left the *Albatross* at Guaymas, Mexico, after being at sea three months, quite enough for one year, he said. More than anything he looked forward to a comfortable bed that did not do acrobatics on the rough seas.

Agassiz made two more trips on the *Albatross* into the Pacific to Guam, Fiji, Tonga, Cook, Society, and Marquesa Islands. The findings of these trips were published in great detail in a volume put out by the Harvard Museum in 1902. In addition to the written descriptions, Agassiz and an artist member of the staff made drawings showing the size, color, and general anatomy of practically every species of animal dredged.

Even if Agassiz had lived three normal lifetimes, he would not have been satisfied with his findings. In fact in 1898 he wrote to Sir John Murray, "I hope to live to be a hundred. . . . I don't hope to, but ought to finish all." He knew there were still great blank areas in the oceans between the lines of soundings and all attempts to chart the Pacific Ocean were tentative and horribly incomplete, with tens of thousands of miles of water without a single investigation. All that he and the other workers had been able to do was to snatch a thimbleful of information from the immensity of the oceans. Yet Sir John Murray said that Agassiz had been a greater inspiration and had done more toward explaining the biological and physical conditions of the oceans than any other man.

During the last twenty-five years of his life Agassiz devoted his money, time, and thought to studying the wonder and beauty of coral reefs. When still a young man, he had roamed about the Hawaiian Islands, visiting the sugar plantations, studying the volcanoes, and marveling at the coral that everywhere fringes the islands.

One evening, while enjoying dinner on the veranda of a sugar planter's home, Agassiz noticed a schooner unloading a cargo of lime in the harbor.

"Why," he asked, "are you importing all that lime?"

"Because we use large quantities of it on the plantation," replied the host, evidently thinking his guest very ignorant.

"Yes, I know," replied Agassiz, "but why don't you make it?"

"Make it? How can I?"

"All the rock around here is coral, pure limestone. All you have to do is burn it."

"My God," exclaimed the host, "And I have been importing it for years," realizing perhaps that a bit of abstract knowledge may have a practical application.

Ever since that casual visit and that casual conversation, Agassiz had wondered about the coral animals that live in shallow waters having temperatures of at least 68° F. between 30° North and 30° South of the equator where they build up islands which lie "like carelessly tossed necklaces on a velvet sea."

The building of coral reefs is one of the most amazing accomplishments of animals, especially when we realize that the individual coral is about the size of the head of a pin. The reefs are not constructed through a spectacular building boom but are the result of a longtime program lasting perhaps thousands of years in which each individual contributes his skeleton as a building block in the construction of huge apartment houses known as an atoll or island.

Roger Revelle says these huge structures are "like Gothic cathedrals, ever building, yet never finished, infinite in detail, yet simple and massive in plan." These minute animals are related to the jellyfish and sea anemones. Unlike them, however, the body of the coral is encased in a cup of hard lime, which the tiny creature extracts from sea water.

Corals reproduce both by budding and by the coming together of eggs and sperm. Budding is the repeated division and redivision many millions of times of the parent animal. Eventually the budding becomes so extensive that the tiny animals live "cheek by jowl" in coral heads of countless number. As the new polyps form, the old ones die leaving masses of limestone just below sea level. In sexual reproduction the eggs are thrown promiscuously into the water where they are fertilized by chance. If the eggs are fertilized, in a few days the eggs hatch and the young larvae swim about from a couple of days to a couple of weeks at the mercy of larger animals, storms, silt, and currents. Those that survive these dangers are carried by currents to some distant area where they pioneer a new colony. The new colony now increases in size by budding and a new coral reef is born.

The coral reefs are sometimes so extensive that many of the South Sea islands are made up entirely of coral growths. Agassiz believed that to understand these great formations would be to understand much of the history of our planet.

Although the beautiful Polynesian islands with waving coconut palms, grass huts, beautiful flowers, and white-tipped waves beating against the shores had long been admired, no one had attempted a precise explanation of the origin of the coral islands until in *Voyage of the Beagle,* Charles Darwin set forth a theory that was endlessly discussed pro and con. He believed that as soon as corals begin to establish themselves along the edges of an island, the island begins to sink, but the corals grow at the same rate as the sinking. The island continues to sink and the coral to rise, until after a million years or so nothing remains of the original island. In its stead is a coral island.

Alexander Agassiz disagreed violently with Darwin on the origin and growth of coral isles, calling him an armchair scientist who had seen one or two atolls. Agassiz believed that corals have played a much less important part in the formation of reefs and islands than Darwin's theory implied. To him a more logical explanation was that thousands of feet below the base of the atoll or reef was an old volcano. Through long geological ages accumulations of silt, shells, eroded material, noncoraline algae, or coral rock settle on the old volcano. When these foundations reach a height suitable for coral growth, the minute animals take up their abodes there and build a relatively thin crust (not more than 150 feet) on the top of these accumulations. Agassiz was so sure that his theory was correct that he offered to prove it by making a diamond drilling through the coral.

Coral reefs became almost an obsession with him. He visited the reefs in Florida, Tortugas, Bermuda, Bahama. Then he was off to the biggest and best reef of them all—the Great Barrier Reef stretching for a thousand miles along the northeastern coast of Australia. For this expedition he chartered the *Croyden*, a small cargo vessel which he equipped with a sounding machine, dredging nets, and provisions to last two months.

Because of very bad weather he was able to work only five days during the entire expedition. Agassiz made only two deep sea dredges on the reef and then the wind was blowing so hard he could not be sure of results. Writing to John Murray he said, "I have never been connected with a greater fizzle." This was a bitter disappointment to a man who had enjoyed so many successful research journeys. He had made his mistake, he realized, by coming to Australia when the trade winds were blowing.

He did not feel that the expedition was a failure, however, for he was entranced by the beautiful species of coral—staghorn, brain, branching, cathedral, organ pipe, stony—each a riot of color: blue-green, yellow, red, purple, brown, white, and black. To add to the beauty, swimming among the corals were fish of rainbow hues, while on the white sand pink algae waved in the moving waters. These beautiful masses of color dwarfed anything Agassiz had seen before. Best of all the lovely corals were in such shallow water he could study them with a simple water box.

This visit convinced Agassiz more than ever that over long periods of geologic time, high cliffs and table lands had been eroded and denuded until they were worn down below the surface of the sea. Eventually they were reduced to flats which became the outer edges of the great reefs. He felt too that it was only during the present geological epoch that corals had obtained a footing on the submerged flats building up the Great Barrier Reef.

In spite of his conviction that his theory of coral reefs was correct, Agassiz chartered a 500-ton steamer, the *Yarella,* to take him to the Fijis, well-known coral islands. In 1897, writing from Suva to Sir John Murray, who held much the same view of coral reefs as he did, Agassiz said, "Hurray, I've gone and done it, as we say in American slang. We have just come from a month's trip around the Fiji Islands and a more interesting trip I've never had. I have learned more about coral islands and reefs than in all my experience put together. But I'll not go into detail here except to say I am more satisfied than ever that each district must be judged alone and that no sweeping theory such as Darwin's can apply to reefs and atolls as a whole."

Darwin and Agassiz carried on a spirited correspondence on the subject of coral reefs. Darwin once wrote to Agassiz, "I wish some doubly rich millionaire would take it into his head to have borings made in some of the Pacific and Indian atolls and bring home cores from a depth of 600 feet for slicing." On his way home from Fiji, Agassiz, the now "doubly rich millionaire," had the opportunity to so oblige Charles Darwin. He happened to be on the spot when an artesian well was being drilled in Hawaii. Down to 80 feet there was nothing but recent coral rock, but from that point down to 1,800 feet the limestone was composed almost entirely of mollusk shells and foraminifera. To Agassiz this evidence completely knocked out Darwin's argument that coral reefs were formed through sinking. Granted they may be formed in several ways, Agassiz insisted that they are brought about through some kind of upgrowth or crowns on volcanic cones. Sad to say for Agassiz's arguments, Darwin's subsidence theory has gained most support, although even today the question of coral reefs is by no means settled. (After World War II United States Navy engineers sank a shaft at Eniwetok to 4223 feet where it struck volcanic rock. This seemed to confirm Darwin's theory.)

After years of investigations Agassiz had satisfied himself about coral reefs. In the winter of 1898–99 at the age of 62 he was back dredging on the *Albatross,* as alert and active as he had ever been. Most of the oceanographic problems he had pursued having been solved and the results published, the indomitable Alexander Agassiz turned his attention to the Polynesian peoples, their customs, handicrafts, and the influence of the missionaries upon them. In a letter to a friend he said that the people were happy without the trappings of material possessions—laughter, music, rhythm, and love were their lives. Brown women with flowers over their ears far outshone their American sisters. In a P.S. to the letter he added that in the Gilbert Islands the ship's officers dreaded to go ashore because the natives insisted on their opening their mouths to show the gold in their teeth.

Fortunately the *Yarella* was on the island of Ovalu in the Fijis when the Bololo, a marine worm which spawns in the last quarter of the moon in November, gave off such quantities of eggs and sperm that the water became as thick as spaghetti soup. At the first signs of the appearance of the worms everyone—men, women, children—took on a carnival air and climbed into boats or waded waist high in the water to catch the worms' delicate eggs, which they ate raw or cooked with breadfruit.

After a couple of hours the worms disappeared as suddenly and as mysteriously as they had come. This great gathering of the worms is the marriage swarm of a species of worms living in the crevices of nearby coral reefs that throw their sex products into the water in response to certain phases of the moon. After the discharge of the eggs and sperm, nothing is left of the worms but their shriveled transparent skins, which almost immediately drop back into the water.

Even at sixty-nine, Agassiz wanted to go to sea once more, still his greatest pleasure. For this trip he secured the *Albatross* for a third and last trip. Away he went on a 13,000-mile journey, around Cape Horn, up the coast of Peru, and over to Easter Island where he viewed the great stone images which Thor Heyerdahl so vividly described in *Aku Aku.*

But it was to dredge that he had come, especially in the Humboldt Current that sweeps past the Galapagos Islands. Because of the rich menu brought to the animals by this current, the tow nets were overflowing with globigerina and diatom ooze, while the dredge brought up hundreds of starfish, crabs, shrimps, sea cucumbers, and fishes. In one dredge twelve species of fish were dredged out of 150 specimens. As soon as the ship was out of the path of the current, however, the waters were a vast desert, producing nothing but manganese nodules, sharks' teeth, and whale bones.

No matter whether the dredge disgorged sharks' teeth, sea lilies, or any of the hundreds of other animals, after thirty years of study of the sea Agassiz was almost as familiar with the contours of the sea bottom as a farmer is with the lay of his own land. Scarcely a species of animal appeared in a dredge that he could not identify at first glance. He could also cite the publication, the date, and the page on which it was described. Nothing puzzled him.

In the months between the rigorous life on an oceanographic ship and the grueling work it entailed, Agassiz lived with his stepmother graciously but not lavishly in the home that his father had bought. On her death in 1907, when Agassiz was away on an expedition, he said, "I can't realize that when I go back to Boston, I am not going to see mother again. From the day I first saw her there never was a word of disagreement between us. She belonged to me and I to her."

Even in his old age Agassiz's first thought was always to build up the collections for the Museum. He would haggle over the price of a riding horse for his own enjoyment, but he would spend ten times that sum for "the fossil remains of its remote ancestor" for the Museum. As we might expect from such a widely traveled, hard working scholar, Agassiz was very popular with scientists. He also had a close circle of friends by whom he was "dined out galore, and lunched and clubbed."

Agassiz's ambition and overall dream was to summarize the results of his cruises, and to sketch in the pieces of the jigsaw puzzle which he had worked so hard to fit together and from them to draw some conclusions about evolution. During his life he wrote 145 important scientific papers. So tremendous were his findings and so varied had been his scientific interests that at one time he had ninety men working on the material. Even with this corps of workers it would have taken many years to present the results of his work to the world. Fortunately his will provided funds for the completion and the publication of his work. Today these researches can be seen and studied in the Harvard Museum of Natural History. In 1900 Agassiz and his sisters gave the University funds to complete almost all of the museum buildings hoped for by their father, Louis Agassiz. In recognition of this gift and Agassiz's long devotion to Harvard, he was made honorary director of the whole museum.

In the autumn of 1909 Alexander and his son Maxmillian went to London, where Alexander presided at a zoological conference. He loved London and had many friends there, but as spring drew near he became restless. He wanted to return home to get ready for his work at Newport. So early in March of 1910 the father and son boarded the *Adriatic* for Boston. On March 21, after an evening of cards and conversation with his shipboard friends, Alexander went to bed apparently perfectly well. Yet so tenuous is the link between life and death that during the night, "Fittingly upon the ocean in whose mysteries he had so deeply delved, his mother, Nature, whispered to him her great secret and led him peacefully and painlessly into the unknown."

✿   ✿   ✿

One man passes away, another takes his place. While Agassiz had been investigating coral reefs in the tropics, Fridtjof Nansen had been icebound in another part of the ocean—the frozen north—on his famous ship, the *Fram*.

5

Fridtjof Nansen — *The* Fram

He sleeps; and the whitest blanket
Wraps him in ice and snow.

"Unseen and untrodden under their spotless mantle of ice the frigid polar regions slept the profound sleep of death from the earliest dawn of time." This is the opening sentence of Fridtjof Nansen's amazing story of the polar expedition of the *Fram* which lasted from 1893 to 1896.

For courage, physical endurance, and good luck the men of the Norwegian *Fram* Expedition have probably never been equaled. "The lucky thirteen," they were called.

Fridtjof Nansen was steeped in the history of the Arctic. Almost by heart he could recount the daring deeds of the Vikings, the Russians, the Norwegians, the Eskimos, the British, the Americans who had tried to penetrate the frozen north. By many paths and by many means, explorers from these countries had attempted to reach the North Pole. Little by little they had learned how to adapt their vessels and their lives to the conditions in this bleak land, but in the end they had always met defeat. Now Nansen was determined to add his name to this long list of explorers. Unlike them, however, he swore he would not accept defeat.

Of all the accounts of polar exploration he had read, the story of the ill-fated *Jeannette,* an American ship under Lieutenant Commander George W. DeLong of the American Navy, had the most important bearing upon Nansen and his plans for a route to the Pole.

It was known that the *Jeannette,* after drifting in a northwesterly direction from Wrangel's Land for two years, was subsequently crushed and sunk in the comparatively low latitude of 77° 15′ North in 1881.

In 1884 Nansen had read a magazine article which stated that three years after the sinking of the *Jeannette* near the New Siberian Islands a pair of oilskin breeches and the peak of a cap on which was written "F. C. Lindeman," a member of the crew of the *Jeannette,* had been found by an Eskimo seal hunter near Julianehaab on the southwest coast of Greenland over two thousand miles from the place where she had sunk. Although there was much division of opinion as to the meaning and reliability of this find, it seemed quite certain these articles were from the *Jeannette.* This set Nansen to thinking. To reach this point the wreckage must have drifted with some unknown current across the Polar Sea over the top of the world. Nansen had no idea what the current was, but he determined to find out. At that moment modern polar exploration was born and Nansen's own plans were made.

Nansen, then in his late twenties, was a giant both physically and mentally. He had the strength of a young horse and an insatiable desire for excitement and knowledge. By the time he was twenty he had earned a doctor's degree in zoology at the University of Christiania (Oslo); since that time he had gained a reputation as a promising scientist and explorer by joining a sailing vessel, *The Viking,* for a voyage to Greenland waters, and by crossing Greenland on foot with Otto Sverdrup, two Norwegians, and two Finns. The party met storms, bitter cold, and all manner of hardships, but

somehow the men always overcame the obstacles. In fact the
difficulties only increased Nansen's desire of reaching the Pole.

Young Nansen did not underestimate the dangers of this undertaking. He knew the Arctic cold was very severe and that the ocean
was covered with a deep body of ice which sometimes piled up into
great towering hummocks and pressure ridges. Between these
were ice floes large and small that were extremely dangerous to
try to push through. Nevertheless, he felt that previous explorers
had only nibbled at the edges of the polar regions by trying to avoid
the ice.

Once caught in it, they or their ships had rarely escaped. Nansen proposed to sail deliberately into the ice. He realized he would
probably be locked in as the others had been, but his plan was to
let the ship drift wherever it would with this mysterious current.
He did not know where the current flowed, but if the materials from
the *Jeannette* had been found on the southwest coast of Greenland,
it seemed logical to assume that, driven by a wind blowing from east
to west, it moved from the New Siberian coast over the Pole, down
to Franz Josef Land, and finally to the coast of Greenland. To drift
with the current over the Pole, that was the answer.

To prepare himself for this great adventure, Nansen studied
maps, read more books, searched old ships' logs, and talked with
everyone who knew anything about the North. By 1892 his plans
were complete. He presented them before the Christiania Geographical Society. The object of the trip, he explained, would not
be to find the exact mathematical point of the North Pole, because
that was of small importance, but to investigate both scientifically
and geographically the great unknown regions that surround the
Pole. Primarily it would be an oceanographic expedition. The plan
of the expedition was severely criticized by the geographers, who
contended it was foolhardy to approach the Pole by an untried
route, especially one so erratic as a current.

However, Nansen's convictions were so strong and his power of
persuasion so forceful that after much debate of the possible success of such a venture, he swept away all objections. The King gave
it his wholehearted support and the Norwegian government agreed
to pay one-third of the cost of the expedition, the rest to be raised by
popular subscription. This was quickly and easily done.

With his characteristic energy Nansen prepared blueprints for
building the ship. The ship, to be called the *Fram,* meaning "push

forward," was to be small—402 tons gross—the overall length 128 feet, extreme breadth 36 feet, draught 15 feet, and displacement 800 tons. She would be built so as to offer as small a vulnerable target to the ice as possible. All in all she was to be built solidly enough to withstand the greatest pressure of ice from every direction, with rounded side walls 24 to 28 inches thick. She would travel both under sail and a 220-horsepower engine. If she were built according to his plans, Nansen believed the force of the ice would lift her up without crushing her between the floes. "The whole craft should be able to slip like an eel out of the embrace of the ice," Nansen assured his backers.

He anticipated every possible emergency both in the construction and the equipment of the ship. He prepared for a five-year expedition, giving special attention to the selection of clothes and food for the crew in order to guard against scurvy and other ailments.

When the expedition was announced, requests from persons wanting to accompany the party came from all parts of the world. From the flood of applicants twelve husky Norwegians were selected. Otto Sverdrup, Nansen's friend from Greenland days, was appointed commander of the *Fram*. The other men were specialists in their fields, but with so small a crew each knew that he would have to turn his hand to a thousand tasks.

On Midsummer's Day 1893 the *Fram* was ready to sail from Pepperviken near Christiania. As Nansen closed the door of his home behind him and waved to his young wife and baby daughter, he thought, "Behind me lay all I hold dear in life. And what before me? How many years would pass ere I should see it all again?"

Amid great acclaim from the Norwegian people, the *Fram* started on her long journey northward, sometimes in fair weather, sometimes in fog and rain. The ship stopped at one or two places to take on sledges, boats, coal, reindeer cloaks, Finn shoes, reindeer flesh, and dried fish for the dogs (which had not yet come aboard).

At Tromso, although it was only July, mountains, plains, and housetops were covered with snow. In Vardo, as a last salute to civilization, the crew members had steam baths in the town bathhouse, and were entertained at a sumptuous banquet with speeches and champagne. The town band had acquired a big bass drum for the occasion.

The next morning amid a wonderful peace and calm the *Fram* set out and all Norway was left behind. On July 27 the ship sailed into dense fog, nothing but fog. She also met the first ice. "So soon?" marveled Nansen. In a few days the ice extended everywhere, but there was nothing to do but "gå fram"—push forward. Trying to free herself from the ice that sought to imprison her, the ship "twisted and turned like a bowl on a platter."

At a tiny Russian settlement on Yugor Strait thirty-four dogs were picked up, all of them barking at the top of their lungs as they waited for their meal of raw fish. Here the last letters were sent home and the last tie with the inhabited world was broken. Having seen the dogs put aboard and witnessed a Samoyede drunken orgy, Nansen set out at midnight for Taimur Strait.

As the *Fram* inched along through the fog, a feeling of utter desolation settled over the men. The only sight was ice and snow, the only sound the cry of loons and the howling of the wind and the dogs. Nansen wrote in his diary, "Now we have open water ahead, now more ice. It is impossible to tell which it is. Is this Taimur Strait? Are we getting through? A whole year is at stake. No, here we stop, nothing but ice ahead. No, it is only smooth water with the snowy land reflected upon it. This must be Taimur Strait." With his inadequate maps before him, Nansen sat in the crow's nest and scanned the baffling white world around him.

September 6, the fifth anniversary of Nansen's wedding day, brought good luck. The fog lifted and the day was bright and clear. Sverdrup thought he could trace a channel into open water. Nansen gave an order to get up steam and head for Cape Chelyuskin, the northermost point in Asia, about 750 miles from the Pole. Never had the *Fram* gone so fast. Without hindrance and as if guided by one lone star (Nansen's lucky omen), the ship passed this dreaded cape. She had escaped one of the most likely places for the winter's imprisonment. Nansen believed that the way was now clear to the drift ice north of the New Siberian Islands. To celebrate passing the cape, the cook prepared a party, the first of dozens of such feasts. The saloon was gaily lighted, and after a many course dinner punch, fruit, and cigars were served. Nansen raised his glass. "Skoal, my lads, and be glad we have passed Chelyuskin."

Nansen took his first series of temperatures and water analyses in this area, the surface salinity (amount of salt) reading twenty-six to thirty per cent; the deep water temperature 29.1° F.; the air temperature 18° below zero F.; the latitude 78° North. The compass pointed north by east, the course on which the whole expedition was based, that of finding a north-flowing current that would carry the *Fram* over the Pole.

The many birds flying about indicated that land might be near, but Nansen did not want to be blocked by land. He wanted to get out into open water. It gave one a strange feeling, he wrote in his diary, to be sailing over water where no man, no ship, no boat had been before, but on flew the *Fram* toward the open seas until September 21, when she met so much ice that she could go no farther.

At first Nansen expected that the ice would soon open up to allow the ship to "gå fram," but in a few days he wrote in his diary, "Frozen in faster and faster. . . . Winter is coming now. Had a visit from a bear, which was off before we could get a shot at it." With good grace he resigned himself to being locked in the ice, for how long he could not guess. The *Fram*, which he hoped would carry him over the Pole and on to the Atlantic Ocean, was at the mercy of that unknown current. However, the long dreaded night had arrived sooner than he had expected.

The first job after accepting the fact that the ship might be locked in the ice for years was to convert her into comfortable quarters and to protect her against the pressure of the ice, the cold, and the wind. The men removed the rudder, took apart the engine, oiling and labeling every tiny part, for they knew lost bolts or screws could not be replaced. They installed a carpenter shop in the hold, a machine shop in the engine room, a smithy on the deck. Even a windmill to provide electric power was set up on the ship. Each day ice was carried to the galley to be melted for cooking, washing, or drinking. Continually there was need for the repair of a hook, a knife, wooden shoes, a bear trap, a water meter, or ice shelters for the dogs. Often a thermometer needed new parts, or a dog harness had to be made. "In fine there was nothing between heaven and earth we could not turn out except constant south winds," said Nansen.

The men were so healthy that except for the weekly weighing and examining them for scurvy, Dr. Blessing, the physician, had nothing to do. To keep himself busy, he took up bookbinding, photography, diseases of dogs, and collecting plankton with Dr. Nansen. The one job everyone worked on was the writing of a diary. Thousands of words were written each day about the bears, the food, or the weather, interspersed with such philosophies as each man's personality revealed.

When the ship had been made comfortable for the long dark night of winter, there began the most important task of all, the taking of scientific observations. Meteorological records were taken every four hours day and night. In fact, for a considerable time they were taken every two hours. These kept one man busy for many hours each day. Every second day the position of the ship was taken.

This was perhaps the most exciting moment of all. The entire crew crowded around to hear the latitude readings. With the drift of the *Fram* a couple of minutes north the men's spirits rose; with each slight drift south they fell. One day she drifted forward, the next back. Once she remained on the same spot for two months.

Temperatures of the surface waters were taken every four hours by inserting a thermometer into a bucket of water hauled on deck from a hole in a narrow channel. With a small sounding machine the deep sea temperatures were taken through a hole kept open in the ice about 150 feet from the ship. Years later, remembering the difficulty and the uncertain results of taking water temperatures on the *Fram*, Nansen perfected a water bottle open at the top and bottom. At a required depth a "messenger" was sent down a wire which flips a trigger to close the bottle. Three walls act as insulating chambers for the cylinder to prevent loss or gain of heat while the bottle is coming up and the thermometer is being read. The Nansen water bottle was also widely used in collecting phytoplankton samples. Now on the *Fram* at depths of several hundred feet the temperature of the water varied from 29.1° F. to 33.8° F. (about as cold as sea water becomes). At the same locations the temperature of the air was so low that the water on the line froze the moment it was out of the water.

It was the investigations that had to be taken below the ice that were most difficult—the formation of the ice, its growth and thickness, and its temperature at different levels; the direction and speed of the currents under the ice; the collection and examination of such life that exists in the northern seas; the amount of electricity in the air; and the magnetic constant. Soundings and dredgings were such an undertaking that everyone had to assist, one sounding sometimes taking several days.

When Nansen started out from Norway he believed, as did most students of the polar regions, that the waters of the Arctic were shallow and interspersed with numerous islands which were a continuation of the American and European continents. He soon found this theory entirely wrong. There were few land masses in the Arctic and the water was deep.

Based on this assumption of shallow water, Nansen had not provided the *Fram* with sufficient wire rope for making deep soundings or dredges. This lack of cable posed a real problem even for the versatile *Fram* scientists. They solved it by making sounding lines from the cables which were to have held the ship to its moorings (no need for moorings in the ice). The cables, only one hundred and fifty feet long, first had to be unwound into separate strands, then two or three twisted together again by hand and soldered. This was a difficult and exacting job in weather twenty to thirty degrees below zero. "Never accept defeat" was Nansen's motto, so after many days' work, the men succeeded in splicing a sounding line 13,375 feet long.

Having made the line by dint of torn and frostbitten hands and incredible labor, the men handled it very carefully, for if it broke there was no material for a new one. In spite of their care, the line soon became brittle and worn from the ice that continually froze upon it. However, in temperatures of 20° to 30° below zero they used it to sound to depths of 1,800 to 2,100 fathoms. Nansen admitted the taking of water temperatures was a doubtful pleasure. Often the "lifter" became coated with ice so that it would not close or the water froze tight while it was being poured into sample bottles. When this happened, the whole apparatus had to be taken to the galley to be thawed out. Just as often the temperatures had to be read by candlelight. Nansen suspected that the freezing affected the reliability of the readings.

In his diary he comments, "Your fingers are apt to get a little stiff and numb when you have to operate ice covered metal screws with bare hands and read the thermometer with a magnifying glass to secure accuracy to a hundredth part of a degree, and then you have to keep the bottle of water samples close to your breast to prevent the water from freezing. It is a nice business."

Nansen also fished for plankton between the blocks of ice at a depth of 150 feet with a silk net. No sooner did he find an opening to slip the tackle through than it began to close and he had to haul it up quickly. Although he often was not able to secure them, he could see through the smallest openings in the ice tiny crustaceans and worms giving off a pale phosphorescent light.

One morning Nansen hauled up the dredge which he had lowered to 800 fathoms the previous day. It contained two pails of mud, which he spent the next two days sieving to extract minute starfish, jellyfish, worms, sponges, and shrimps. Judged by this sounding he believed that there was not such a scarcity of life in the Arctic waters as one might expect, but the difficulty was in securing them.

The days differed but little from one another—breakfast at eight with bread, cheese, corned beef or bacon, oatmeal, biscuits with orange marmalade or jelly, coffee, tea, or milk. Three times a week there was fresh bread and often cake. Dinner and supper were equally bounteous. The food was so delicious and plentiful that Nansen wrote in his diary, "We looked like fatted pigs. One or two of us began to cultivate double chins and a corporation."

After working hard all day at a thousand tasks, the men relaxed after supper by smoking or reading books given to their library by friends before leaving home. Later in the evening they played cards or the accordion, or someone ground out on the mechanical organ "Oh, Suzanna" or "Napoleon's March across the Alps in an Open Boat." On those evenings the saloon became a little oasis in the vast desert of ice.

Before going to bed most of the men put on their reindeer coats and fur gloves and went on deck to look for bears, a never-ending source of entertainment, and to watch the Aurora Borealis with its eternally shifting loveliness, there being nothing more glorious than an Arctic night. Nansen wrote, "It is a dreamland painted in the imagination's most delicate tints; it is color etherealized. It is a dream, a glimpse into the realms of fantasy. One shade melts into the other, so one can not tell where one begins and the other ends, and yet they are all there." Then he adds, "What depth of beauty with an undercurrent of endless sadness there is in these dreamily glowing evenings."

Peter and Juell, two of the "lucky thirteen," continually argued about the thickness of the ice under the *Fram*. Peter maintained it was at least twenty feet thick, while Juell bet twenty kroner that it was not that thick. One night they decided to resolve the argument by drilling through the ice. Unfortunately the borer reached no further than sixteen feet. Peter, however, agreed to cut away with an ice pick the four feet that were lacking. Dripping with perspiration he worked until midnight. Several times a little water gushed up, then he struck ice again. Just short of twenty feet water again spurted from the hole.

Juell shouted, "The twenty kroner are still mine." Not convinced, Peter sank a line through the opening and at 30 feet it again struck ice. The men had to give up the wager, but both were convinced that the *Fram* was lying on a sizable chunk of ice. (No doubt the men were boring into a deep pressure ridge.)

This great sheet of glass was not a level covering but was broken into great hummocks that looked like mountains, with channels between them. Sometimes the ice blocks crashed and pressed against one another and against the ship with such force that the *Fram* was lifted up many feet, then dropped with a thud. As the winter advanced, great hummocks of ice piled high on all sides of the ship, while loose snow drifted and swirled in every direction.

At times it seemed the *Fram* could not withstand the onslaught any longer. "There is something gigantic about it. It is like a struggle between dwarfs and an ogre in which the pygmies resort to cunning and treachery to get out of the grasp of one who seldom relaxes his grip," Nansen wrote. The pressure Nansen believed was related to the cycle of the high and low tides. Sometimes the pressure became so violent that the men prepared to abandon ship, carrying everything they would need for survival far out on the ice. But the pygmies had built the ship so strongly that the *Fram* always kept afloat and wiggled herself free from the embrace of the giant.

When the ogre did not succeed in grinding the *Fram* to powder it tried other tactics. It tried to bury her. An ice floe split in two, forming walls almost as high as the ship's masts on all sides, squeezing and pressing endlessly. Then for several days the ice would relax its grip and the men went back to work.

The *Fram* had now been at sea six months. There were twenty-four hours of night without a sign of daylight. To compensate for the sun, the moon raced around and around the sky day and night. Only the electric lights brought a touch of civilization into the frozen ghostly world. The newly formed surface ice froze fifteen inches in fifteen days. The general average temperatures were 30° to 40° F. below zero. By this time the men had become so accustomed to these temperatures, they rarely had a fire in the stove and went on deck to read the thermometers in their shirt sleeves.

Christmas Day dawned. The thermometer read 36° F. below zero. There was an endless stillness of an Arctic night. How the men longed for the sound of a Christmas bell. The only means of celebrating in this icebound wilderness was to eat, and eat they did, bounteously and often. After a five-course dinner, cakes, toddy, and cigars added extra cheer. No one thought of supper. Then came the presents, gifts which the *Fram* had carried all the way from Norway—a knife, a pipe, a knick-knack. Yet these trinkets were received with childish pleasure. To hide his homesickness each man laughed a little louder or told an extra joke. It was a strange Christmas to these home-loving Norwegians.

Perhaps Nansen felt the frustration and the loneliness more deeply than the others, for that night he wrote at length in his diary, "Add to this the good cheer of a good strong ship, good entertainment, and then a good sound sleep. What more can one wish? But how I long to return to life. Let me get home again, as conqueror or beggar. What does it matter? But let me get home to begin life anew."

By February 1894 the *Fram* had drifted to 80° North Latitude. In September 1893 she had been at 79°, a movement of but one degree in five months. Nansen was desperate. At that rate the party would not be home for eight years. He could not endure this tortoise-like progress much longer. He must break through the darkness, the inertia, and find some outlet for his energies. A plan began to form in his mind.

If there were no other way of reaching the Pole, surely a couple of men could get there on foot with dogs and sledges. (A number of the early explorers had used dog sledges.) The weather wouldn't be any colder than it was here and for protection from the winds they could pitch a tent behind a snow hummock. Having reached the Pole and made their observations, they could no doubt find their way back in the direction of Franz Josef Land, Spitzbergen, or the west coast of Greenland.

Nansen argued with himself that he had come to the Arctic to explore the unknown polar regions. His countrymen had given him their money to do that, not to sit on a drifting ship becoming fat and lazy. He tried to put this wild idea out of his mind. It was unthinkable that he would desert his shipmates; but the idea would not be downed.

As the months passed the darkness began to lift. Each day the sun shed its golden fire down warmer and warmer. In May the temperature rose almost to the freezing point several times. The men cleared the snow from the *Fram's* decks. The ice began to melt and the pools of melt water dotting the ice sheets grew wider as the warm Arctic sun shone down. The water in the pools was almost fresh enough to drink. Spring had come. But the ship continued to seesaw, first north, then south.

Nansen took plankton tows between the blocks of ice. He became so interested in these small creatures, particularly the diatoms, that he turned his whole attention to the world of the microscope. Beneath the crust of ice he also found the water teeming with infinitesimal animals that he imagined had the same instincts, the same struggle for existence, perhaps the same pleasures as we have.

The diatoms, which formed brownish patches on the ice, are one-celled plants so small that a teaspoon can hold a million individuals no larger than a pin prick. These infinitesimal bits of life brought Nansen untold pleasure and wonder for the microscope showed that each diatom is enclosed in a glasslike box, the top and bottom fitted together so perfectly that it looks like a crystal basket filled with jewels as the strands of sparkling protoplasm and amber pigment catch the light. Diatoms reproduce by cell division, which is conducive to rapid production of enormous numbers of individuals. (Today the electron microscope, which can magnify a hundred thousand times, reveals amazing facts about a diatom.)

In winter the diatoms formed resting spores and took refuge from the cold by sinking into the ice, becoming embedded ever deeper as the ice thickened. Now as spring arrived the diatoms which had slept in the ice began to stir, forming brownish patches on the pools which the men called "Dutchman's 'baccy juice." Other minute algae were carried toward the light. Among the diatoms and algae were microscopic animals so small that they could be seen only with a high powered microscope. Also mixed with these tiny bits of life was a little mineral dust, but in general life in the frigid North was very sparse. The surprising thing was how any life could exist under the overwhelming odds of the Arctic seas.

Nansen had neither the techniques nor the knowledge for identifying microscopic marine life, but he gathered and preserved the tiny forms carefully and later on his return to Norway he sent the material to Professor H. H. Gran, a specialist in diatoms and other microscopic algae, who described eighty-four species from these icy waters.

Dr. Blessing, the patientless physician, often went with Nansen to look for animal and plant life. On Whitsunday a gull paid the *Fram* a visit. Then birds of many kinds flew about. One day after searching for hours, they came across a *Converva*, a chainlike green alga, attached to the ice by slimy threads. As the summer advanced, quantities of chainlike greenish-red algae popped up through the ice or from the edges of the floes.

The search for diatoms, slimy green algae, and infinitesimal animals floating on the polar seas may seem of little scientific importance. But Fridtjof Nansen and his men were determined to gather all possible information, however trivial, about the North. They knew that they would not pass this way again. They knew too that however insignificant each discovery was in itself, the sum total of their findings would help to put in place pieces of the jigsaw puzzle from a part of the world hitherto almost completely unknown.

Like all modern scientists, Nansen believed observations should be so accurately taken that scientists a hundred years hence could, if necessary, use them with confidence. He was very conscious, however, that because of the difficult conditions of polar research and his ignorance of what to expect in a totally unknown sea he was not always able to achieve complete accuracy. Yet the careful investigations and precise recordings made on the *Fram* as recorded in six volumes of findings are today considered important milestones in oceanography and Arctic research. (They were particularly valuable to the *Nautilus* and the *Skate*, nuclear submarines which passed over the Pole sixty-five years later.)

All the time Nansen was studying diatoms and algae, another part of his mind was mulling over the plan of setting out over the ice on foot and dog sledge. He rationalized that without him the ship's crew would continue to make the necessary scientific observations, and he believed that the knowledge he would gain farther north would many times outweigh in value that which he would make here. He had also come to suspect that the *Fram* would never drift across the North Pole. For it to do that he should have entered the pack ice farther east.

Without telling anyone of his plans, Nansen attempted to get himself in training for a possible journey by making daily snow-shoe runs across the ice. He also ordered the men to snowshoe each day from 11:00 A.M. to 1:00 P.M. as long as the light lasted. They built six dog sledges and six kayaks, each weighing sixty pounds, big enough to accommodate two men and a couple of dogs, and strong enough to carry equipment and provisions for one hundred days. (All Nansen told the men was that it might be necessary for them to make their way home across the ice.)

Nansen kept an especially anxious eye on the twenty-eight dogs. All his hopes were centered on them. Each day they had a run on the ice, but they were in no condition for heavy sledge hauls. Several of the dogs had died; two had been killed by bears. Eight puppies had been born on the *Fram.* These small creatures, which were an unending source of interest to the men, would soon be ready for sledge duty. Nansen now confided his plans to Sverdrup.

October tenth was Nansen's thirty-second birthday. The temperature was 24° F. below zero, with snow packing again and the roar of the ice deafening. But no matter what the weather or how busy the men, a birthday must be celebrated. For supper that night the saloon was decorated with flags. When Nansen walked into the room, the men stood up and sang, "Many happy returns." The cook served a dinner of fish pudding, sausages, tongue with potatoes, beans and peas, preserved strawberries with rice and cream, crown extract of malt, and two drams of liquor. As a special treat Nansen passed his precious cigars (he was down to the last box). A couple of the men danced a jig to the accompaniment of the accordion. The saloon resounded with laughter and jokes. In tribute to the party Nansen said "Many a worse birthday has been spent in lower latitudes than 81° North."

Later, sitting in his cabin, warm, comfortable, reading and smoking, he listened to the storm tugging and tearing at the riggings and the snow whirling in every direction. He had a feeling of guilt as he compared his comforts with the sufferings of the earlier Arctic explorers. In spite of his apparent satisfaction with his life, before he climbed into bed he wrote in his diary, "Sometimes I almost seem to long for a defeat—a decisive one—so that we might show what is in us and putting an end to this tiresome inactivity." To Nansen this inactivity was really neither life nor death, but a state between the two.

Months rolled on. Nansen's idea of setting out for the North

Pole on foot took more concrete form. With pencil and paper before him, he plotted his proposed journey step by step. From the *Fram*'s present position at 83° 47' North he assumed the Pole was about 483 miles away. With each dog carrying 75 pounds of the 2,100 pounds total load and traveling nine and one-half miles a day (about the distance he had traveled over the ice in Greenland) the trek to the Pole would probably take fifty days.

Of course the load would be diminished somewhat every day by consumption of supplies. Some of the dogs might have to be killed for food or the provisions might be lost or they might run out. If worst came to the worst, he figured, any reasonable person should be able to subsist by hunting bears, walruses, or sand hoppers. (How little he then knew of the frozen North.) After every possible obstacle had been considered, Nansen still felt sure he could reach the Pole.

In his supreme confidence he estimated that, having reached the Pole and planting the Norwegian flag there, he would walk back in the direction of Cape Fligely, the nearest known land to the Pole, which he thought was about 370 miles from it (it was probably nearer 500) and he would eventually reach Franz Josef Land or Spitzbergen. Of course he would make meteorological and biological observations along the way.

Finally his plans were complete and he had to tell the men about this great adventure. Hjalmar Johansen was chosen to accompany Nansen. Sverdrup would stay on board, make the oceanic observations, and during the next summer try to get the *Fram* free of the ice.

Amid a thundering salute from the *Fram*, Nansen and Johansen, after several trial runs, set off for the great unknown on March 14, 1895. The first few days on the ice, as they had anticipated, they walked between seven and nine miles a day. The temperatures averaged 45° F. below zero. Then the unexpected began to happen. In this intense cold the men's clothes became an armor of ice by day and wet bandages at night, the ice melting while they lay swathed in the heavy sleeping bags.

As the days dragged wearily by, the sleeping bags became terribly heavy to carry from the moisture which froze on them. Each day the blankets became more soggy. To conserve body heat the two men, drying their socks on their chests, slept in the same bag. Slogging across the ice became increasingly difficult until they could travel only two or three miles a day. The continual lifting of the sledges over the hills of snow was enough to tire out giants. When they could not walk another step, they threw up their tent behind a hummock of snow and without eating crept into the sleeping bag. If they attempted to eat, they fell asleep with the spoon raised half way to their mouths. Next morning they scarcely had the energy to crawl out of their moist cocoon.

On April 8, Nansen and Johansen stood on a hummock of snow at 86° 10′ North Latitude, 195 miles closer to the North Pole than any man had stood before. The temperature was 25° F. below zero. In every direction stretched a desolate waste of hills and ridges of ice that looked like ocean waves frozen stiff. Since the men had left the *Fram* they had not seen a trace of life in the air or on the ice—no bears, no walruses, no sand hoppers. They had apparently passed the limit of life.

What should they do? The situation was becoming desperate. Several dogs had already died and food was becoming scarce. Nansen felt sure he was within 224 miles of the Pole. He couldn't bear to give up. Yet he knew it was no use to try to go on. So he made the most difficult decision of his life. He decided to turn back.

For a few days, in walking away from the Pole, the situation was somewhat better than going toward it. Often they started about two in the afternoon and kept going until one in the morning (there is no difference between day and night during an Arctic summer). After a few days they were slowed to a crawl again by hummocks or stopped by channels of water. Every hummock was a crisis, every melt pond a detour. Nansen's defeat had come all too soon. And by heading south all incentive was gone. To add to his troubles, he had let his watch run down (he stayed in his sleeping bag too long), and he could no longer accurately measure longitude. He hoped that he was headed for Franz Josef Land, but he had no way of knowing definitely.

The fifty days that he had estimated for reaching the Pole had long since gone. In early June food had to be rationed. Nansen shot a gull, but he couldn't afford to waste ammunition on such small game. The dogs were so ravenous that they chewed the reindeer straps, the sailcloth harness, and the wood from Johansen's snowshoes. Along with the dogs, the men were always hungry and always wet. The poor beasts had to be driven forward with a whip. One by one they had to be killed. There were only six left.

One day Nansen made a pudding from the blood of his own lead dog. Then their food problem was solved. They shot a seal. They feasted for breakfast on seal stew. For dinner they fried a seal steak which Nansen said could not have been surpassed in the finest hotel in Christiania. For supper Johansen made blood pancakes fried in blubber.

But food could not satisfy Nansen for long. He could not live by bread alone. On June 30, 1895, just two years after the *Fram* had sailed from Norway, he wrote in his diary, "Here we lie far up in the North, two grim, black soot-stained barbarians, stirring a mess of soup in a kettle and surrounded by ice and nothing else." There was no energy or equipment for scientific work. Johansen shot another bear and her two cubs.

On and on the two men trudged—until July 24 when they saw land. Above the white line of the horizon rose a glacier-clad mountain. They could hardly believe their eyes. "Land, land!" they shouted. They had not seen land for nearly two years. It was like a vision, like a fairy land. But the glaciers were many miles away and the cliffs so sheer and formidable that they could not land on the ice-bound coast.

The last two dogs were killed. Not until thirteen days later, August 7, did they step on bare ground. What land was it? Nansen had no idea. The country was terribly bleak and inhospitable. Although it was only August the long winter night was already settling in. The men did not dare to push on. Using their hands for tools, they built a hut ten by six feet from the debris found at the bottom of the cliff, the tent serving as a roof. Above the hut they hoisted the Norwegian flag (the one they had hoped to plant on the Pole).

And the "barbarians" knew they would not starve, for there were bears on shore and seals and walruses in the water. When Nansen could rouse himself from the sluggishness of eating and sleeping, he made a whole new wardrobe out of bear skins. Nine months passed. It was spring again—May 1896. Once more the men forced themselves to try to find human habitation. Leaving behind them everything not absolutely necessary to sustain life, they used the last kayak to get across the melt ponds, but they carried it more than they rowed it.

One morning in June, having clambered onto a rocky shore to prepare their walrus breakfast, Nansen thought he heard the bark of a dog. A dog? Was it possible? He pulled on his snowshoes and dashed off in the direction of the barking, his heart pounding furiously. Soon he thought he heard a human voice.

In answer he "hello'd" with all the strength of his lungs. An answer came. Soon two men stood face to face. That night Nansen wrote in his diary, "One was an Englishman in checked suit, well shaved, well groomed, bringing with him the perfume of scented soap; the other a wild man, clad in dirty rags, black with oil and soot, with long uncombed hair and shaggy beard, with a face in which the naturally fair complexion could not be discovered."

"Aren't you Nansen?" asked the Englishman after a moment of disbelief. "I'm Jackson of the Jackson-Harmsworth Polar Expedition. By Jove, I'm glad to see you." He seized Nansen's hand and shook it heartily.

"Where are we? I've been completely lost," admitted Nansen.

"At Cape Flora on Franz Josef Archipelago. We're trying to find out how far Franz Josef Land extends and if it is a land route to the Pole." (Of course it was not.)

Taking Nansen by the arm, Jackson said, "Come with me. We have plenty of room for you and any companions in our Russian timber hut. And we are expecting our ship, the *Windward*, from England any day now. It will take you to Norway."

After a bath, a haircut, and a shave, Nansen and Johansen settled themselves in comfortable chairs in that hut. A feeling of complete peace came over Nansen. Through the bark of a dog all his troubles, all his responsibilities, were swept away. He was on land, warm, comfortable, clean, and among friends. The hospitality of the Englishmen was boundless.

After years of mental apathy Nansen loved the heated discussions before the great fireplace. The men talked about diatoms, polar currents, the origin of fjords and continental shelves, bottom deposits, treking over the ice, and all the other problems of the North, problems of which almost nothing was known but which were a tremendous challenge to these early students of the North. Probably they argued the longest about the formation of continental shelves, those narrow ledges of land that extend to a width of 30 miles and a depth of approximately 600 feet from almost every large body of land in the world.

Were these shelves formed from wastes from the land or from erosion? Some of the men argued that in regions where great quantities of material from the land are carried into the sea, this waste fills up and levels the sea bottom and protects the coasts against the attacks of the waves. The more waste carried from the land, the broader the shelves, as is seen at the mouths of the Amazon, the Mississippi, and the Siberian rivers.

But might they not be formed, argued others, by the force of the waves gnawing and grinding at the land? For example, the broad shelves of the Faroe Islands, the Newfoundland Banks, and the English Channel were no doubt worn down by erosion, sometimes out of solid rock both at the surface levels and far down in the water. Still others suggested that in tropical regions corals no doubt help to build the shelves. This is a piece of the jigsaw puzzle that had not yet been put in place. (Today most geologists believe that the continental shelves are formed both by deposits from the land and by erosion.)

Nansen of course was particularly concerned with the path of the currents in this area and where they might have carried the *Fram* since he left her more than a year ago. The men gathered around the fireplace in Jackson's Russian hut endlessly discussed the currents. They felt sure that the climate in the North was definitely influenced by the unusual pattern of currents and the circulation of the water, but they had not had enough experience with the currents hidden far below the layer of ice to predict their course. They did know that the surface current with low salinity and low temperature is about 600 feet deep with a velocity near the surface from 0.5 to 1.0 mile in twenty-four hours. (No wonder the drift of the *Fram* was maddeningly slow.)

They knew too that below the surface current is an undercurrent of high salinity and relatively high temperature running in the opposite direction from the surface current. Below 1,200 to 1,500 feet the temperature decreases downward but without reaching the temperature of the upper polar water. At 2,500 to 3,000 feet the temperature rises again, probably owing to the heat from the interior of the earth.

In the true ice-covered polar regions, the unusual current patterns and surface temperature ranges prevent much growth of plankton. Yet just south of the thick ice blanket where the cold water of the north meets the warmer water of the south there is as summer approaches a sudden and explosive outburst of life in the plankton (the food staple of many fish and whales). In fact, these waters produce the greatest fisheries in the world—Iceland, Lofoten

Islands, Norway, Denmark. Here too live great whales that feed on the abundant plankton.

Several theories were put forth to explain this great explosion of life. Dr. Nansen believed that the chemicals—nitrates, sulphates, silicates, and others—accumulated in the water. These materials are absolutely necessary for the development of plant life, but since there are so few plants in polar waters, the minerals are not used up. Therefore they accumulate in great quantities. When the polar ice begins to melt, the minerals are carried to the Atlantic by the currents. Then, as the surface water is freed from the ice and heated by the sun, the abundant chemicals bring about a great outburst of planktonic life, which in turn provides a rich feast for the fish.

Although Nansen was greatly stimulated by these discussions, his thoughts were most often of home. "Dream, dream of home and beauty. Dream a golden dream of future reunion," kept ringing in his head. Was this dream a delusion too, he wondered as the weeks passed and the *Windward* did not arrive.

It was not until July 26 that the long-looked-for ship, the *Windward,* steamed into Cape Flora. After the excitement of the ship's docking had died down and the provisions that were to last the Englishmen—who were to stay in this lonely outpost for two years more—were unloaded, the letters brought on board, and the men leaving Cape Flora settled in the cabins, the captain raised the gangplank. He wanted the ship well on its way south before the winter storms began howling again. Hardly able to hide their elation, Nansen and Johansen bade farewell to their hosts who had given them such a cordial reception.

The *Windward,* trying to make her way between the islands, was stopped several times by ice floes. But at last she came to open water. One morning, when Nansen came on deck, he saw in the distance a bare and naked shore scarcely more inviting than the one he had left in the mist of the Arctic Ocean; but it was Norway. Nansen was beside himself with happiness. Norway, his beloved Norway. Soon the *Windward* came into the harbor of Vardo. On the dock were people, dozens of them. He had almost forgotten how the civilized world looked.

Almost before the *Windward* dropped anchor, Nansen climbed into a small boat and was on his way to the telegraph office where he sent off a hundred messages, the first to his wife, whom he had thought of almost continuously since he left home (she joined him in Vardo a couple of days later), the second to the King of Norway, and the third to the Norwegian government. The next day congratulations of good will poured in from every part of the world. From all the flagpoles in town and from the mast of every ship in the harbor waved the Norwegian flag. (The same band and drummer as three years before turned out to greet Nansen.)

Almost as if by a miracle a few days later Nansen received a telegram from Spitzbergen, "*Fram* arrived in good condition. All well on board. Will start at once for Tromso. Sverdrup."

All Nansen could say was, "The *Fram* has arrived. The *Fram* has arrived. They got free of the ice. How did they do it?" As fast as time and space could get him there Nansen reached Tromso. A short distance offshore lay the *Fram,* strong and broad and weatherbeaten. The last time he had seen her, she was half buried in ice. Now she floated proud and free on the blue waters of Norway.

After more than a year and a half the "lucky thirteen" were together again. The men all talked at once. "Tell us. Tell us everything." There was a very bedlam of talk. Finally Nansen called for silence. "Stop all this unimportant chatter and tell us how the *Fram* got free."

"By hacking and chopping away at the ice, day after day, month after month," Sverdrup explained. "And by exploding dynamite a few feet from the ship. In August 1895 a terrific rainstorm had loosed the coating of ice on the rigging which clattered to the deck like sheets of steel." That was the beginning. . . .

Another winter passed; Sverdrup recalled that during the spring of 1896 he blasted the ship a number of times with as much as 100 pounds of dynamite. With each blast more ice was loosened and the faithful *Fram* edged forward a bit. At the end of twenty-eight days of crawling, she dodged between the last blocks of ice. The *Fram* was free.

Free. After thirty-five months of imprisonment. The rest was easy. On August 20 at 2 A.M., 1,041 days since the men had last seen land, the *Fram* reached Skjaervo. Sverdrup made a beeline for the telegraph office and pounded on the door. The station master stuck his head out of the window above the office and roared out, "Hello, what's the matter? Deuce of a noise to make at this hour of the night."

However, the name of Sverdrup and the *Fram* were magic words that opened all the telegraph circuits in Norway. The *Fram* had come home. Such a celebration as was given the town had never seen.

Now, in Tromso, as the members of the *Fram* crew reviewed their long sojourn in the North, Nansen felt that she had fulfilled her mission. He had not reached the mathematical point of the North Pole, but he had traveled within 224 miles of that mythical spot. He knew that instead of being a shallow body of water enclosing many islands, the North Polar Sea was large and deep, for he had sounded it to 12,000 feet or 2,000 fathoms. Nansen was convinced there was no land near the Pole from which icebergs could originate. He felt sure that there was a slow current flowing under the ice traveling in the same direction as the ice but that the ice overlaying the water produced strange patterns of water circulation.

He still held to the belief that a current that might some day provide a sea route passed over the Pole from the south. (Sixty-five years later U.S. nuclear submarines *Nautilus* and *Skate* passed under the ice at the Pole with William Anderson and James F. Calvert as captains.) He knew that, although there was little marine life in the upper polar waters, microscopic diatoms and algae survive being frozen in the ice for months.

Nansen had proved without a doubt that man's ingenuity permits him to build ships strong enough to resist pressures and thunderings of the great forces of nature. His men had proved that human beings can endure the most extreme cold, hunger, and physical deprivations, and that an adequate and varied diet can completely overcome scurvy, dread disease of seamen. He had helped establish the geographical position of Franz Josef Land. In short he had investigated the great unknown regions of the North and had lifted much of the mystery that surrounded the top of the world. However, the North Pole still slept under her spotless mantle of ice.

In spite of his accomplishments, at thirty-six years of age this active, restless, ambitious man, Fridtjof Nansen, was not ready to forsake the sea. Within the next few years he made half a dozen oceanographic expeditions into the Arctic Ocean; from Iceland to Ireland and back to Norway; through the Kara Sea to Siberia and the Amur region; through the North Atlantic to Portugal, Madeira, Azores, and back to Norway.

Between these expeditions he prepared six large volumes in

which he gave a detailed account of the *Fram* trip; and he made scientific researches into physical geography. (It was during these years he perfected the Pettersson-Nansen water bottle, still widely used for shallow water.) He also served as Professor of Oceanography at the University of Christiania. During World War I, when it was impossible to make oceanographic expeditions, Nansen took up politics, interesting himself particularly in methods of furnishing relief on a large scale to displaced persons.

He worked with Herbert Hoover, the Red Cross, and the League of Nations. As High Commissioner of the League, he helped to bring about the resettlement of great numbers of Russian, Armenian, and Greek refugees, and the repatriation of 500,000 prisoners of war from Siberia, China, and other parts of the world. For these splendid accomplishments, Nansen was awarded the Nobel Peace Prize in 1923. He died at the age of 69 in 1930. Fridtjof Nansen was a man of forceful personality, the strength of whose character shone through every page of his remarkable book, *Farthest North*, "as light through a stained glass window." I have quoted freely from *Farthest North* because of the vivid picture that the book presents of the author and the detail of life on the good ship *Fram*.

✻   ✻   ✻

In 1896 when the *Fram* returned from Farthest North, the polar seas were not yet ready to give up their secrets. But oceanographers were wondering how deep the sea really was. In 1910 Sir John Murray set out on the *Michael Sars* to find out what animals lived in the depths of the Atlantic Ocean.

6

Murray and Hjort — *The* Michael Sars

And the depths of ocean its presence confessed.

It was now 1910. Thirty-five years had passed since the *Challenger* had returned from her historic oceanographic trip around the world. John Murray, now Sir John, had deposited the fifty volumes of the *Challenger* report in the British Museum; the *Challenger* office in Edinburgh had been closed; and the endless stream of visitors who had come from the ends of the earth to see and marvel at the collections had dwindled to a mere trickle. The house that Murray had bought near the office for his wife and five children and for entertaining the visitors was surprisingly quiet.

Sir John was feeling lonely. He wanted to go to sea again.

What matter that he was seventy years of age. Probably it was only an excuse for an expedition, but he said he wanted to test the validity of the findings of the *Challenger* in the light of the great advances in techniques and improved equipment for the study of the sea in the intervening years.

To urge the need for a reappraisal of this material and a more scientific study of the North Atlantic, Murray attended the International Council for the Exploration of the Sea in Copenhagen, where the suggestion for such a study was eagerly accepted by the Council. As a start on this undertaking Murray offered at his own expense to charter the *Michael Sars*, a 225-ton ship built in 1900 for scientific work, particularly for the investigation of Norwegian fisheries.

Murray did not expect the *Michael Sars* to bring back the wealth of material the *Challenger* had done, but he hoped that the expedition would make a very definite contribution to our knowledge of the seas, particularly of the life on the floor of the ocean and in the intermediate waters, phases of oceanography that he had been interested in since *Challenger* days.

He realized no ship would ever reveal such wonders or arouse such interest as that famous old ship had done, for it was the first of the great marine expeditions. In fact it sailed away from England on an experimental journey in 1872 and four years later brought back a new science.

Of all the cargoes ever carried into a port, without doubt the strangest were the tons of seashore life dredged from the floors of all the oceans of the world. Probably the most amazing discovery was the adaptation that the animals of the sea make to the conditions under which they must live and their ability to emit a cold green-blue light that can dispel the eternal darkness of the pitch-black ocean floor.

These and many other remarkable findings of the *Challenger* convinced the world that scientists had somehow stumbled upon a wonderful new realm of life and had opened up a limitless field of research. These discoveries were just as marvelous and exciting in the 1870's as is the exploration of outer space ninety years later.

In the thirty-five years between the return of the *Challenger* to England and the outset of the *Michael Sars* Expedition in 1910 many daring men had extended the knowledge of the 71 per cent of the earth's surface covered by water. They had learned that the area of the oceans is two and a half times as great as is the area of the land. Yet the oceans provide three hundred times the habitable space that the land and the fresh water areas do. On land, plants and animals can live only a few feet above the earth's surface and a very short distance beneath it. But the seas are inhabited by at least some form of life from the surface down to 37,000 feet, the very nadir of the earth.

Too, a close relationship exists between water and the animals that live in it. The water bathes both the outside of the body and the cavities within it. Because the physical conditions of the water and the concentration of the dissolved salts change but slightly, marine animals do not need to develop highly specialized systems to protect them against sudden changes in environment as man does.

In other ways too the sea is a good place to live. Since water is essential to all life and makes up 80 per cent of active protoplasm, it carries in solution oxygen and carbon dioxide, which are absolutely necessary for the growth of plants and animals. This gives marine animals great advantages over land animals against being dried out. There is never a drought in the sea. Too, because sea water holds heat a long time, danger of rapid changes in temperature is done away with. The transparency of water also makes it possible for plant life to exist relatively deep in the water.

Within the ocean also is a wide range of living conditions. The salt concentration varies from almost fresh water near the surface to concentrations of 37 per cent at lower depths. Temperatures range from 80° F. to the freezing point.

Light intensities vary from brilliant sunshine at the water's surface to absolute and eternal darkness in the ocean depths; pressures vary from 16 pounds per square inch at sea level to many thousands of pounds on the deep floors of the ocean. However, the pressures do not have much effect upon the animals since an equilibrium exists between the inner and outer pressures of the body tissues.

In like manner the continuous movement of the ocean waters benefits the animals within it by providing oxygen at all depths, by removing wastes, dispersing plant foods, spores, eggs, and larvae. In fact, the currents serve as a most efficient transportation system within the oceans for both adult animals and their larvae.

The inhabitants within this astonishing world vary as greatly as do the environments that support them. Undoubtedly the earliest life on this planet was the tiny plants that were carried about in the surface waters. Then came the small animals that fed upon the plants. From those simple beginnings have arisen all other forms of life up to and including man. Of the larger groups of animals called phyla (those animals having fundamental characteristics not possessed by those of any other phylum) by far the greatest number are found in the sea. Of the seventeen phyla all are represented in the sea, yet several of them have no representatives on land, the starfish and its numerous relatives, for example.

Through the thousands of soundings that had been made, it was known that the floor of the oceans was on the average two and one-half to three miles beneath the surface of the waves; that huge ridges and mountain peaks rose from submerged plains to within a few hundred feet of the surface, sometimes even sticking their craggy heads above the water as volcanic islands or coral atolls. In fact, Jacques-Yves Cousteau, the French aqualunger, recently suggested that life within the seas is so pleasant that an experiment is being conducted in which man will be born, live, and die in the sea.

All this and many, many more secrets had been wrested from the sea in the years since the *Challenger* had sailed away from the dock at Sheerness. Probably no body of information had been gathered under more difficult conditions of weather, toil, frustration, and uncertainty, but the dedication of the early oceanographers, their patience, and their visions had changed man's whole concept of that "great waste of waters" that is the ocean. Each expedition—Swedish, Norwegian, Russian, American, English, or German—had done its part in unraveling the web of the sea. But the *Challenger* remained the ideal of them all.

The name of Wyville Thomson will always be known as the driving force back of this pioneer expedition, but much of its success goes to John Murray, a young naturalist to whom Thomson assigned the responsibility of preserving and arranging the materials, and as the man who after Thomson's death directed the specialists in the classification and description of the enormous collections and who saw to the publication of the results. The post expedition work took five times as long as it did to collect the materials.

John Murray was born March 3, 1841, in Canada, but he was a typical Scotsman in all his ways. At the age of seventeen his parents sent him to Scotland to live with his maternal grandparents to complete his education. He attended the University of Edinburgh, enrolling in the medical school, yet he ranged widely over many fields, picking and choosing classes that appealed to him: natural science, heat conductivity, and chemistry. John Murray never took a university degree and probably never intended to, but later in life no man had more honorary degrees conferred upon him by universities and learned societies in Europe and America.

In 1868 a whaling ship, the *Jan Mayen,* was bound for the Far North. The ship was badly in need of a surgeon, so because young Murray had once been a medical student he was hired for this important job. The ship reached 81° North Latitude and landed at such remote points as Spitzbergen, Jan Mayen Island, and other Arctic ports. The men on the ship were remarkably healthy, so Murray had time to make collections of marine animals, record temperatures in air and water, make observations on currents, and study the distribution of ice. During the seven months' voyage, Murray became fascinated by the problems of the ocean. Upon his return to Scotland he wandered for two years up and down the coast studying many phases of marine life.

Then quite by accident he became a member of the *Challenger* staff. Almost at the last minute, one of the naturalists was not able to make the trip and Murray was appointed to take his place, a very happy choice both for the great work of his life and his contributions to science.

During the years that the *Challenger* collections were being prepared for publication, Murray did the work of half a dozen men and plowed through an unbelievable amount of detail.

William Herdman forty years later tells in *Founders of Oceanography* how he and a group of other young men gladly spent their free afternoons helping in the endless work of arranging the collections. Under Murray they learned to distinguish the oozes and saw such wonders as deep sea cucumbers and dark red prawns. "These are now commonplaces of marine biology, but then they were revelations and those of us who witnessed the discoveries in the making will always associate them with 'Challenger Murray' as the arch magician of the laboratory, a sort of modern alchemist, bringing mysterious things out of store bottles and showing us how to determine their true value."

During the twenty-five years that Murray was busy with the *Challenger* materials, he somehow found time to be active in every new investigation in the rapidly growing science of oceanography, until by the turn of the century he was no doubt one of the best known and most active oceanographers in the world. Even in his busiest years he did not give up the strenuous work at sea. He loved to rough it, never complaining, however difficult or primitive were the accommodations of the ship or the methods of work.

An expedition that gave him great satisfaction and produced very important results was one to the Faroe Islands in 1882 on the *Triton* to investigate the strange contrasts in temperature and fauna there. Ever since the *Lightning* and *Porcupine* expeditions, when Wyville Thomson had first studied the waters around Scotland, he had suspected that the Faroe Channel was separated into two distinct regions, one warm, the other cold, but he did not live to make a thorough study of the area.

Many years later on the *Triton* Murray and his co-workers found that the warm and cold areas of the Channel were separated by a high mountain range that rose to within 200 to 300 fathoms of the surface. Each side harbored its own group of animals with almost no contact between them—cold Arctic forms on the north and warm Atlantic forms on the south. Of 216 species recorded from the warm area and 217 species from the cold side, only forty-eight were common to the two areas. Murray named this the Wyville Thomson Ridge. This ridge was an excellent example of the effect of environment on the distribution of marine life and their adjustment to physical conditions under which they must live.

Johan Hjort, the great Norwegian oceanographer, said nothing had done so much to awaken interest in oceanic research as the discovery of entirely different animals on the two sides of the ridge. In fact, this discovery impressed Murray so strongly that much of his work in later years was devoted to studying the factors that determine the distribution of animals.

Another project in which Murray combined pleasure and hard work was the trawling, dredging, and temperature observations of the deep sea lochs of the western Scottish Highlands on his steam yacht, the *Medusa*, in the company of a young friend, Frederick Pullar. Unfortunately young Pullar was drowned on one of these cruises, but his father, Laurence Pullar, provided funds and a staff of scientists to complete the work. They made 600 soundings in 562 lochs. The results of these soundings were published in six volumes dedicated to Frederick Pullar.

Proof that purely scientific investigations sometimes become successful commercial enterprises was shown through a *Challenger* discovery made in 1875 when Murray found large deposits of phosphate on Christmas Island in the Indian Ocean. At the time his interest in the island was only in relation to coral reefs. He later realized the phosphate deposits had economic as well as scientific value. He persuaded the British Government to annex this lonely uninhabited island far from the main highways of the world and to grant a concession to work the products to a company which he formed. The project was highly successful, both to the nation and to the company. After the company had operated but a few years, the government had received more money in royalties and taxes from the phosphate than had been the entire cost of the *Challenger* Expedition and the publication of results.

In the years between the expeditions of the *Challenger* and the *Michael Sars* cruise of 1910 at least six thousand deep sea dredges and trawls had been made, most of them in the Atlantic. Alexander Agassiz and several other men had also investigated the Pacific, where in 1899 the Nero Deep had been located close to the island of Guam 31,614 feet below the surface, only 66 feet less than six miles deep. This exceeds Mount Everest, the greatest known height above the level of the sea by 2616 feet.

But the questions—how deep the oceans really were, what the bottoms were like, what conditions existed there, and what animals lived in the eternal darkness—were still largely unanswered. John Murray was determined to find the answers to these and hundreds of other questions, if humanly possible. At seventy he had so little time left.

Both Murray and Hjort knew that if these questions were to be answered and the expedition was to be a success, much depended upon the scientists who made up the group and upon the mechanical and scientific apparatus used. Therefore they chose the most highly trained specialists in each branch of the work and installed on the ship the most modern instruments—centrifuges, reversing thermometers, water sampling bottles, and otter trawls.

By the first of April 1910 all was ready, and the *Michael Sars* sailed from Bergen to Portsmouth where Sir John Murray joined her. To Murray's great delight, the *Michael Sars* was under the command of his old friend Johan Hjort. In honor of the cruise the scientific men of England entertained the Norwegians royally, giving dinner parties, receptions, and interviews. The partying over, the ship left England on April 7 for the southeast of Ireland; thence it worked down the western coast of Europe as far as the Canary Islands, across the Atlantic to the Azores, and back to Newfoundland. It then recrossed the Atlantic to Bergen by way of the Faroe Islands.

During the four months' cruise the *Michael Sars* traveled 11,555 miles; set up 120 stations; lowered 900 miles of wire rope with four winches; recorded data on currents, temperatures, and winds; and dredged thousands of species of animals from all depths.

When the ship was back in Norway and there was time to assess the results, both Murray and Hjort agreed that the cruise had been a success. Above all it had proved that the conclusions drawn from the *Challenger* Expedition and other early cruises were extremely reliable. Yet it had shown that to date scarcely a dent had been made in understanding the "One Great Thought" that controls the operation of the seas. It could still be said that studying the depths of the ocean was like hovering in a balloon high above an unknown world hidden by clouds. More especially it had given Murray an opportunity to investigate in greater detail a number of problems which of necessity he had only superficially studied during the *Challenger* cruise when he had had his baptism into deep sea dredging.

Murray and Hjort planned to bring out the specific results of the cruise in a series of studies published in Bergen. However, they placed the most valuable record of the trip before the public in 1912 in the book *The Depths of the Ocean.* Although it is primarily the story of this particular expedition, it is also a general account of the modern science of oceanography as it was then understood, yet a work still so sound and scientific, and so readable, that it is almost as widely consulted today as when it was published fifty years ago.

Life in the deeps, those areas more than 3,000 fathoms below the surface, had always intrigued Murray. The great deeps cover a relatively small area, perhaps nine million square miles. They are found in all the oceans. But twelve thousand deposit samples from waters below 1,000 fathoms had been examined by the *Challenger* office. These showed that the bottom was covered with both organic and inorganic materials.

Red clay, the general name for the inorganic deposits, is a composite of minute manganese nodules—probably the "fallout" of meteors, decomposed rock, and products synthesized in the bottom of the sea. The red clay is found at depths beyond 2000 fathoms and is the oldest and most widely distributed of all the deep sea deposits. The organic deposits on the floor of the sea are of plant and animal origin (the same claylike material brought up in John Brooke's first dredge)—pterpoda, diatoms, radioiarians, globigerina. The globigerina ooze, the most widely distributed animal deposit, is a soft, dirty, white material composed of the shells of many species of foraminifera and of deep sea mollusks.

Through the centuries the shells of these minute organisms have fallen slowly, silently, from the surface waters where they spend their few hours of life to the graveyard on the bottom where they build up ooze at the rate of about one inch in ten thousand years, though the rate is influenced by temperatures, currents, and materials transported by floating ice from some glacial period.

While on the *Challenger*, Murray, perhaps the earliest man to do so, realized that the ooze had a dramatic story to tell of the long history of the planet. Yet with the instruments available in those early days he could bore only eighteen inches to two feet into it. (Today ocean scientists are attempting to drill through the earth's crust down to the mantle—a minimum of 18,000 feet.)

Even in 1910 it was very difficult to say with any certainty what animals actually live in the dark, cold, forbidding floor of the oceans, because before the *Michael Sars* Expedition all attempts to gather material from the deep ocean were made with a trawl or net that not only picked up materials from the ocean floor but, while being lowered or raised, filtered an immense column of water from the bottom to the surface, making it impossible to determine which animals came from the bottom and which came from the intermediate layers.

For many years an argument had waged as to whether the great body of mid-water was inhabited or whether life was limited to the upper and lower levels only. Both Wyville Thomson and Alexander Agassiz believed that the mid-oceans were devoid of life.

On the *Michael Sars* this piece of the jigsaw puzzle was partially put into place by the use of a series of nets which automatically closed at different levels, thereby showing the depth from which a specific animal came. Two lines and a number of nets were used at the same time, silk nets for plankton and other tiny forms, and cotton nets with graduated meshes for bigger animals. The nets were attached to lines at intervals of 50 to 150 feet down to 3,000 fathoms.

A three-horsepower winch (a drumlike contrivance usually operated over the side of the ship for raising or lowering the dredge or trawl) was used for deep animals and a one-horsepower winch for shallow species. The closing of the nets was controlled by a meter equipped with dials and a clock for measuring the amount of wire played out and for ascertaining the strain on the cable.

When the sea was calm and the currents were slow, the operation of the lines and the various nets worked well and saved a great deal of time, provided one set of nets was lowered while another was being hauled in. When there were strong winds or tides, the nets were apt to collide and tangle.

Even at best, sounding at great depths was a long tedious job. For instance, at 5:45 A.M. on July 31 near the Azores, seamen lowered one of the multiple dredges to a depth of 2,500 fathoms, on 4,000 fathoms of steel wire. (The cable must be long enough to allow for the drift of the ship.) They started trawling at 11:20 A.M. Hauling in began at 2:50 P.M. and the apparatus was back on deck at 9:00 P.M., the actual trawling time being six hours and ten minutes.

In the deepest net, which presumably had raked the deep ocean floor, were worms, sponges, mollusks, sea cucumbers, starfish, dark red shrimps, and jet black fish, animals that were fixed on or at least crept on the bottom.

In the very deep seas there are no seasons. Everywhere is blackness, cold, and ugliness. No plants are produced. The animals are carnivorous, feeding perhaps on one another and on organic wastes originating in the surface waters. Yet Murray did not believe that there was a universal deep sea fauna, for life in the abysses is limited by many factors. Some animals are equally at home on any kind of bottom, others require rocks, while others select soft sediment for their homes. Currents also distribute the larvae of bottom dwellers from place to place, as well as dislodging full-grown animals such as shrimps and amphipods, which creep as much as they swim. Few of these deep sea forms ever reach the surface.

No matter what criterion was used to determine the animals on the ocean floor, both Murray and Hjort agreed that uninhabited marine deserts extended over vast areas. The richest haul taken from the deepest water contained only thirty-nine fishes.

But what did the series of nets tell about the distribution of animals scattered through the waters, those living between 500 to

2000 fathoms? This water is pitch black, inhabited by animals that never touch the bottom nor reach the surface. Yet it is all inhabited, if only sparsely in the greater depths. (It is also a region on which little study has been made.)

The deep areas of the oceans, those over a mile deep, are continuous with one another over all the world. (The Arctic Ocean is an exception.) As John Murray had expected, almost every kind of swimming animal was brought up from the deep open waters in the automatically closing nets. Actually sixty-five species of jellyfish, sixteen of them new to science, were taken from the mid-waters. Of special interest were the great numbers of small fish that moved about in waters at 1,000 fathoms or more. In all, about one thousand specimens of open water fish were captured by the nets. The most characteristic inhabitants of the deep seas are the large scarlet shrimps. However, there were many species of planktonic crustaceans, particularly the copepods, in mid-water. The copepods, no longer than the head of a pin, are the most abundant creature in the oceans and are the food of many animals, including the abundant herring.

Squids and cuttlefish abound in deep waters, but it seems that whales, sharks, and the great fishes never venture as deep as 600 fathoms. A few primitive unsegmented worms with long proboscises for capturing prey were taken far out in deep water. Interesting adaptations made by fish living in the sparsely inhabited deep open areas are the great increase in the size of the mouths and the development of fishing devices, such as barbs with complicated luminous lures at their ends.

In addition to the animals that spend their lives swimming back and forth in the deep ocean waters, the eggs and larvae of sea cucumbers, barnacles, crabs, and shrimps drift through the deep waters, but when they mature their wanderings are over, for they sink to the bottom where they remain the rest of their lives.

Although the mid-depth of the sea is a difficult area to study, having no bottom and no top, the *Michael Sars* scientists added a great deal to our knowledge of the open seas, especially of the small forms that can be caught in the closing nets. Sir Alister Hardy recently said, "The ocean depths are full of problems yet to be solved."

While John Murray was studying the horizontal and vertical distribution of animals in the deep sea, Bjorn Helland-Hansen, physicist of the ship, was busy observing all sorts of facts about the colors, the eyes, and the luminescence of the animals. The brilliant colors of marine animals had always fascinated fishermen. They knew tropical surface fish wore either sky-blue garments or transparent robes, and that herring were blackish-brown when seen from above but were silvery as they flashed through the water. They knew too that most deep sea fish were black, violet, brown, or red. How could they possibly acquire colors that were as varied and beautiful as those of the rainbow?

Many attempts had been made to explain the exotic colors, the most logical being that they were attempts of animals to adapt themselves to the color of their surroundings; another was to hide from enemies; or perhaps they were for sexual attraction. Helland-Hansen agreed the animals' desire to make themselves inconspicuous might be true in part, but he felt sure the color was dependent upon the intensity of light at different levels (the accepted theory today).

To test his theory of the intensity of light he exposed photographic plates at different levels. These showed that at the surface light rays of all color were present, although at 30 feet there were few red rays. At 1,500 feet there were many blue rays, but the green rays were gone. At 3,000 feet a tiny trace of light could be seen, but at 3,500 feet not a ray of light was visible.

In surface waters near the Sargasso Sea, Helland-Hansen saw that most animals were transparent. For instance, the eel larvae were completely transparent, even the blood being colorless, the only spots of color being their tiny black eyes, as minute as pin points. A short distance below the surface were blue flying fish and silver and blue "men of war." The herring, which lives somewhat lower, when looked at from above was blackish-brown. Only when it made a sudden turn did the herring become visible, its mirror-like sides then giving off a silvery flash. (The ocean always looks dark and black when seen from above.) At 1,000 feet many species of fish had silvery sides and brownish backs, while at 2,500 feet there were only brown, dark blue, violet, and black fish and dark red prawns. Below 3,000 feet, where all traces of sunlight were gone, the animals were black or dark red, showing this deepening of color coincided closely with the loss of light.

Jellyfish, for example, were colored in relation to the depth at which they lived. Those living highest in the water were transparent except for a spot of pigment on their stomachs; the next lower group had a dark border along the edge of the bell as well as on the stomach; in those still deeper brown pigment covered the lower side of the bell, but the gonads were still visible; in the lowest group the entire jellyfish was enveloped in a black cloak. A seahorse from the Sargasso Sea had a brown-green body the color of the weed, but the fins which moved freely in the water were a dark blue. Johan Hjort suggested that the connection between light intensity and peculiarities of coloring may result from a physiological process of assimilation.

It is difficult to imagine what real value color can have for animals in the deep sea. Both Hjort and Helland-Hansen agreed that much more work must be done on the color of marine animals before it is fully understood.

Even more amazing than the brilliant color of deep sea animals is their ability to emit light. Hjort said Norwegian fishermen distinguish between "dead phosphorescence" and "fish phosphorescence." In the former, myriads of tiny flashes of light like the twinkling of stars in a clear sky now increase, now decrease in intensity. In "fish phosphorescence" balls of light flare up like electric bulbs being turned off and on. These balls of light are produced by large fishes or squid rushing through the water in warm seas. Often the impetus of their movements causes all the minute plankton organisms (dead phosphorescence) to glow in response to the irritation produced.

In practically all groups of marine animals from the protozoans to the vertebrates the light is produced by glands, which secrete a luminous substance. In some of the higher animals the light organs become very complex. In these the light is projected through a transparent lens in front and a concave reflector behind which appears to be under a nervous control. In the lower animals the light organs are simply luminous cells and the light is without focus or control. This is the type of light we see trailing a rowboat on a summer evening and is given off by millions of luminescent cells on the animals' bodies.

What purpose the light serves has been a matter of controversy among scientists for a long time. Can it be explained as a simple consequence of metabolism (the process by which foods are built up) and the light itself serves no purpose? Or does the light serve as a distinguishing marking? Could it be to illuminate the surrounding waters, to avoid enemies, to help animals in recognizing their own kind, or to attract the opposite sex? No one could say. Whatever the purpose it is undoubtedly intended to be seen by an eye. With the discovery of reflectors and lenses in the eyes of deep sea animals, it seemed quite certain their function was to project light in definite directions.

This naturally gave rise to the question of how the light is produced. It is known that animal light is the most efficient light in the world, for with it there is almost no loss of heat. In man's electric lights half the energy is lost as heat. In the glow worm only one per cent is so lost. Since light organs are found almost wholly in marine animals (fireflies and glow worms are exceptions to this statement), salt was thought to be necessary for the production of light, and perhaps the slime made by the luminous glands involves a chemical reaction. Although even today the processes involved are but partly understood, the light is thought to be brought about by complicated chemical reactions. However it is made, both Johan Hjort and Bjorn Helland-Hansen concluded the light must be of vital importance to the animals and to the survival of the species. Surely nature would not have gone to so much trouble making lights if they serve no purpose.

If the light produced by animals in the great open seas is intended to be seen, then the animals must have eyes. Here we run into even greater trouble, for to the *Michael Sars* scientists nothing in the study of marine animals seemed more hopeless than tracing any real pattern in the development of eyes. The size and structure of eyes of the deep sea fishes varied from those with large eyes to those with very small eyes, while some were totally blind.

The scientists wondered too if there might be a relationship between the shape of eyes and intensity of light. Transparent fish living in the uppermost layers of water had stalked eyes, while telescopic eyes which point upward were found in fishes from depths of 1,500 feet and in those which are poor swimmers. Perhaps this type of eye is best adapted to receive the faint rays of light which penetrate the dusky depths.

The anatomy of the eyes and the pigment of the retina indicated that the eyes were constantly being adapted to seeing in regions of utter blackness. Again we ask whether the size of the eye decreases with increasing depth and, if so, whether the number of blind animals is not far greater than was generally supposed. Yet to contradict this theory the *Michael Sars* scientists found that many fish living in the deepest black waters have large well-developed eyes. It was all very complicated and confusing.

About the only thing that seemed quite certain was that the fishes on the sea bottom possess eyes but no light-bearing organs; on the other hand, the invertebrate bottom animals have luminous light organs but no eyes. Again the scientists wondered what good eyes are if there is nothing to look at on the monotonous ocean floor. These hard working men did not for a minute suppose any definite conclusions had been reached concerning light organs and eyes of deep sea animals on the short *Michael Sars* expedition, but certainly they had raised many interesting subjects for further investigation.

In addition to whatever benefits the animals derive from their eyes, their natural light, and their color, they certainly are aided in their struggle for existence by having huge mouths, long pointed snouts, expandable stomachs, and long sensitive tentacles armed with hooks.

Professor H. H. Gran, another Norwegian scientist on the expedition, attacked the distribution of marine life from another angle—that of the plankton and its importance in the economy of the sea. If these drifting creatures did not have the power to keep themselves from sinking into deep water, the ocean would become a lifeless desert, because in the surface layers live the plants which are the food staples of hordes of animals. Without question the surface plants which form "the pastures of the sea" are more important in the economy of the sea than are the animals, for all life either directly or indirectly is dependent upon plants. In other words the plants are the producers, animals the consumers.

No one knows exactly how plants are produced, but under the influence of sunlight and chlorophyll inorganic substances are transformed into living plant substances. The marine plants, because they take their nourishment from the sunlight and chlorophyll dissolved in the upper layers of water, live within a couple of hundred feet of the surface, the greatest number being produced in water 90 to 100 feet deep.

The one-celled plants, one-celled animals, and a few larger drifting animals, together with the larval stages of more highly developed creatures, such as barnacles, shrimps, starfish, clams, snails, and all the other animals that drift about in the surface water at some stage in their lives are called plankton.

Not only is the plankton the food of other plankton animals, but it is the bread and butter of mature animals that can not go in search of their own food—barnacles, clams, tunicates, worms, as well as of most widely roving whales and fishes. Those plankton forms that escape the mouths of the larger creatures die and their remains sink to the bottom of the sea just as small specks of dust fall to the bottom of a tumbler of water. These swirling particles are often referred to as "snowflakes." Sometimes the water is made murky by the great numbers of carcasses and shells that drift through it. Eventually this material reaches the ocean floor where much of it is eaten by the scavenger animals that crawl over the bottom, as examinations of their stomachs show.

The snowflakes that are not eaten by the bottom animals form a carpet of ooze on the ocean floor. Layers of ooze laid down millions of years ago show that the shapes of these minute creatures are practically unchanged through the ages.

As the *Michael Sars* steamed back and forth across the Atlantic, Professor Gran found that the plankton was not distributed evenly through the seas, scarcity or plenty being determined by light and warmth, by winds and currents, but particularly by chemicals in the waters. In the spring when there are many nutritive salts in the water there is a great outburst of plant life, which then amounts to three-fourths of the plankton population.

Soon many of the chemicals in the surface waters are used up. When this happens, the plants decrease and the animals increase. (In like manner our flowers do not thrive without chemical fertilizers.) By autumn the chemicals are partially replenished through the circulation of the water, and the plant population is built up again. Because of another chemical deficiency during the winter, the plants are again outnumbered by animals.

After a long series of tests, Gran concluded that on a yearly average probably fifty-six per cent of the plankton were plants and forty-four per cent animals. He also believed there may be more plants in the water than are known, many of them so small they can not even be detected with a centrifuge.

Some years before the *Michael Sars* cruise, Victor Hansen of the German Plankton Expedition actually tried to count the plankton, but he could find no reliable gauge by which to measure the organisms in a given spot at a given moment. He knew the production of plankton must be tremendously rapid or else it would be inconceivable that so many animals at all depths could live upon it.

He estimated at least a third of the plankton forms, probably numbering in the billions, are eaten each day. (I wonder if an I.B.M. machine might not have trouble recording such astronomical numbers.)

Professor Gran's studies revealed many new facts about plankton, but today, fifty years later, scientists are still trying to piece together the full story of these small bits of life which are perhaps the most important food factor in the sea.

After reading the account of the 1910 *Michael Sars* Expedition as told in *The Depths of the Ocean,* one will never again be indifferent to what lies beneath the shimmering curtain that is the surface of the sea. The authors have made the story of the distribution of strange and wonderful animals of the deep very real. He who reads it will never think that the ocean is a great waste of waters inhabited by a few fish. He will know it is a world teeming with life, as densely populated as is the land.

The reader will want to pry into the depths himself, to trail a dredge behind a ship, to centrifuge and to isolate the tiny plankton organisms, to dream of some day seeing with his own eyes the ever-changing colors of the animals as they descend to the deep ocean floor, to see the flash of their cold lights, and to philosophize on the meaning of this strange world.

He will be conscious of the rhythm of the tides, the rhythm of the new and full moon, the rhythm of spring and autumn, and the effect of this rhythm on the marine animals.

Sir John Murray returned to England from the *Michael Sars* Expedition refreshed in mind and body and firmly convinced of the reliability of the *Challenger* conclusions. At seventy-three he was as busy as ever writing *The Depths of the Ocean* and *The Seas,* a short popular discussion of the oceans. He dredged, sounded, played golf, motored, and enjoyed his friends. However, on March 14, 1914, he was instantly killed in a motor accident.

Although Sir John Murray will always hold an important place in the history of oceanography, he will also be remembered for his inspiration to young scientists, his humor, his upright character, his genuine kindness, and his commonsense.

All these characteristics made John Murray a dominant figure in any group of people. Whether he was dredging, telling a story, or entertaining his friends, his blue eyes danced, and his good Scots tongue was kindly as well as sharp. Above all he was a broad-

minded scientist to whom every phase of nature was a challenge.
A great and inspiring oceanographer was gone.

        ✿   ✿   ✿

Not only the distribution of animals on the floor of the Atlantic
Ocean but the great whales that rush through the waters of the
little-known Antarctic regions claimed the attention of the tireless
oceanographers.

7

Sir Alister Hardy —
The Discovery I

A whale ship was my Yale College and my Harvard.

In spite of the cold, the winds, the silence, the monotony, and the incredibly hard work, a man who has gone to the far reaches of the sea and who has drawn aside the curtain that separates the air and the water is never quite the same again.

Forever after he says with John Masefield, "I must go down to the sea again, to the vagrant gypsy life. To the gull's way and the whale's way where the wind's like a whetted knife." Or as Roger Revelle, Director of Scripps Institution of Oceanography, asks, "Why is it so pleasant to be on a small oily, uncomfortable ship far from the nearest land?" "Because," he answers, "on shipboard both the past and the future disappear. Only the present is left. You can't do anything about the past and the future depends upon the unpredictable whims of sea and ship."

To these and hundreds of other men, the attempt to fit together the seemingly endless pieces of the jigsaw puzzle of the sea becomes a challenge and the correct placement of each tiny bit a spiritual triumph.

Such was the challenge that drove the *Discovery* to the cold, bleak, little-known South Atlantic in 1925. The avowed purpose of the expedition to the Falkland Island Dependencies was to study the whaling industry, especially the strange relationship of the tiny plankton to the gigantic whales. But to Alister Hardy and other British scientists, it was to investigate many phases of the region and to try to unravel the great complex of the water and the life within it.

In 1925 the *Discovery* was already an old ship, experienced in the way of Antarctic research. She had been built in 1901, when interest in the polar regions was spurring many adventurous young men to seek fame by attempting to conquer the poles.

Interest in the North Pole had driven man to the Arctic for centuries, but interest in the South Pole had lagged far behind, probably because the Antarctic was far from the centers of civilization. There were no human beings within thousands of miles of it, nothing but mountains of snow and ice.

Not until the late 1400's when Prince Henry of Portugal pleaded with scientists and seamen to venture farther and farther south had anyone dreamed of investigating this far-away part of the earth. Prince Henry, who was interested in every phase of the seas, believed that the shortest route to India and the riches of the Orient was by rounding the tip of Africa. But seamen feared the great open waters, which they said were filled with dreadful monsters, burned like fire, and ended in a bottomless abyss. Prince Henry died in 1460 before his dream of sailing around Africa became a reality.

However, the Cape of Good Hope, so named because Henry had hoped for it so long, was discovered by Bartholomew Diaz in 1488; South America was rounded by Magellan in 1520. Thus a route to the East and West was established. Having rounded the tip of these continents, explorers seemed to be content. For a long time there was no further search for what lay still farther south. Then geographers began to talk of a possible continent somewhere far to the south.

However, the great eighteenth-century explorer Captain James Cook convinced them and the world that there was no such southern

---

continent. In 1773 he had crossed the Antarctic Circle as far as 67° South Latitude at 39° 35′ East Longitude, but he had seen no land masses. Therefore, he said emphatically there were none. In 1840 James Clark Ross, a British naval officer, sailed into the Antarctic and discovered Ross Sea, where he dredged to a depth of 400 fathoms. Even his push into the southern waters did not engender much enthusiasm. Interest again lagged.

In the 1850's Matthew Maury, the Pathfinder of the Seas, urged exploration of the Antarctic, saying, "As little is known about the Antarctic regions as about the interior of the moon." It was not until twenty years later that Maury's plea was heeded by the *Challenger* Expedition, which on its almost global tour reached the Great Ice Barrier and crossed the Antarctic Circle at 78° 22′ South Latitude, opposite Queen Elizabeth Land, but the *Challenger's* field of interest was so broad that the Antarctic received but little of her attention.

Once more oceanographers lost interest in the Antarctic until late in the nineteenth century, when it was sparked by two men of entirely different temperaments, John Murray and Clements Markham. For both these men the Antarctic was the last great unknown region in the world. Murray, the scientist, wished to bring about a greater understanding of the oceans through continuous and systematic exploration of the whole southern region with all the instruments of the modern investigator. Markham, who loved the romance and excitement of exploration, wanted a dramatic rush for the Pole. Finally, realizing their views were diametrically opposed to one another, Murray quietly withdrew his plan for an expedition to the South.

With the backing of the Royal Society, Markham persuaded the Admiralty to build a wooden ship, the steam bark *Discovery*, to explore the Antarctic waters. Twenty-eight year old Robert Falcon Scott, a protégé of Markham, was appointed leader of the expedition. The *Discovery* sailed from Cowes in August 1901 with the firm determination that, after traveling as far as possible by ship, Scott and his party would make the long difficult trek to their goal up the icebound South Pole plateau on foot and dog sledge.

In spite of a stormy trip, many encounters with wind and fog, the *Discovery* reached the Ross ice shelf; the men sighted King Edward VII Land and saw a range of mountains stretching far southward and buttressing a vast plateau. Then the *Discovery* was locked in

the ice for two years. During this time Scott, with Ernest Shackleton and Dr. E. A. Wilson, attempted to climb to the Pole over the
vast plateau. They reached a height of 9000 feet at 82° and 17'
South Latitude, where they were turned back by the great frozen
land masses, terrific winds, and unendurable cold.

After a long agonizing trek back to the ship, Scott in 1904 made
his way around the Cape of Good Hope and, in spite of his failure
to reach his goal, returned triumphantly to England. Although he
was probably more interested in geography and exploration than
in the scientific results of the cruise, his men made many oceanographic observations that were published in a series of volumes, and
they stand as a tribute to the great strides that Scott's men made in
Antarctic science.

During the next few years the race and the competition for the
mythical poles became bitter. After attempts by many ill-fated
expeditions, the North Pole was located by Robert Edwin Peary, an
American Navy Commander, April 6, 1909. "The North Pole at last.
The prize of three centuries. My dream of twenty years," said
Peary as he planted five flags (including the Stars and Stripes of the
United States) at the Pole.

Now the race for the South Pole began in earnest. Scott set out
on a second voyage, and Roald Amundsen, having been thwarted
by Peary in his dash for the North Pole, turned his ship (Fridtjof
Nansen's Fram) around and headed for the South Pole. Amundsen
succeeded in reaching it on December 14, 1911.

As if by a cruel fate, just seven days after Amundsen planted the
Norwegian flag on the Pole, Scott's party reached it too. Imagine
the disappointment as they ascended a small rise and saw the black
tents left by Amundsen dotting the snow. This was a bitter blow
to Scott, but he had to accept the evidence of sledge tracks, skis, and
dogs' footprints, and the compass, as proof of Amundsen's victory.
That day he wrote in his diary, "All the daydreams must go."

Deeply depressed, Scott and his small party began the long difficult journey back to the Discovery. The ice was almost impassable.
Early in February because of sickness, insufficient food, and the
severity of the weather two of the party died. Finally Scott and the
others could struggle no longer and within a short time they too
died. Six months later a search party found their bodies in their
snowed-up tent 105 miles from the ship. On display in the British
Museum are several pages of Robert Scott's diary, the successes and

the defeats of the journey all recorded in Scott's beautiful firm handwriting. But near the end of the story the entries became weaker and more shaky until at the last they were almost illegible.

The conquest of the poles, both North and South, seemed to many to be the end of polar exploration, but to the scientists the exact location of the poles was of small importance compared to the scientific knowledge to be gained in the far-off seas.

The accomplishments of Scott and the tragic end of his expedition became a sort of legend in Britain. Along with his diary, a model of the gallant ship stood in the British Museum. The ship herself had been sold to the Hudson Bay Company for commercial fur trading in the Arctic. In recognition of Scott's bravery, sentiment for the old ship was revived in 1923 and scientists became interested in procuring her again. Why shouldn't the *Discovery* make another expedition to the South, this time not for geographic exploration but as a research ship?

The scientists knew such a cruise could in no way be likened to the heroic undertaking of Captain Scott, for in the years between many advances in equipment of research ships and understanding of Antarctic conditions had been made. The party would not suffer the trials and the hardships of those earlier pioneers. The greatest difference, however, was that the men would be concerned with the conditions within the water itself, in the completely unknown South Atlantic, specifically the whaling industry of South Georgia and the Falkland Islands Dependencies.

The dangerous business of whaling had been practiced in France since the tenth century, but the records of whale hunting by the English go back only to 1600. Since that time most of the countries of the world had sent out whaling ships. So determined had been these whalers to capture the huge animals, many of the whaling grounds had been depleted by overfishing. By the beginning of the twentieth century the southern oceans were the last profitable whaling grounds remaining.

In 1904 the British established the first whaling station in South Georgia. The next year they set up a floating laboratory for the extraction of whale oil. Soon dozens of companies from many countries were at work there. By 1921 the whaling industry in South Georgia and the Falkland Islands Dependencies had become the largest in the world with over 3,000,000 barrels of oil being taken between 1909 and 1918.

During World War I, when whale oil was much in demand for making glycerine for ammunition, the capture of the whales was tremendous. In one season 11,792 animals were captured in this area alone. Never before had whaling been practiced on such a scale, and it was feared that the animals would soon become extinct if regulations were not enforced to control their take and a thorough scientific study made of the life history of these mammoth animals.

To provide information about whales and whaling the old *Discovery* was indeed bought in 1923. However, a much wider program was planned for the ship than how whales were caught, cut up, oil was rendered, and fertilizer extracted. The scientists in England realized that if the future of the industry were to be assured, it was necessary for them to understand practically the whole science of oceanography—the temperature and chemistry of the waters, the direction and speed of the currents, the food and feeding grounds of the whales, and the life history of the animals themselves.

Although the *Discovery* was almost entirely rebuilt for its new role, it remained a square-rigged barque with auxiliary steam power and carried a limited supply of coal. Yet as far as possible the scientists hoped to carry on the traditions of the original ship. For the study of oceanography it was equipped with the most modern dredges, trawls, echo sounders, reversing water bottles, and thermometers. Also, in planning a five-year program for the study of the complicated life history of the whales, the best brains of England were recruited. Stanley Kemp was chosen Director of the Expedition, and Alister Hardy head zoologist, both outstanding young scientists.

After two years of rebuilding, the ship sailed from England October 5, 1925, stopping at Las Palmas, Canary Islands, and arriving at Capetown, December 29. In his youthful enthusiasm for his first visit to tropical waters, Alister Hardy said of the passage: "Who will ever forget the first catch at a depth of 1000–2000 fathoms, the tow filled with the richness and beauty of deep sea life—fantastically shaped fish studded with light-bearing organs and patterned and colored like Turkish carpets; deep sea tunicates 6–9 inches long made of a jellylike substance glowing with a brilliant blue light; or while crossing the equator passing through great areas of living lanterns, millions and millions of them, leaving a path of light behind them; or of delicate jellyfish flashing brilliant lights that looked like showers of submarine rockets."

As soon as the *Discovery* reached South Georgia she made a survey of the waters from the surface to depths of 1000 fathoms— soundings, temperatures, chemical analyses, vertical plankton hauls. The scientists saw at once that the work would have to be divided into two parts. The first part of the work would be done on the whales themselves and would be carried on almost entirely at the whaling station at Grytviken on Cumberland Bay, South Georgia and at the nearby biological laboratory. This phase of the work would include detailed observation of the physiology of the whale itself—breeding seasons, time of pairing, period of gestation, number of young at birth, length of sucking period, nature of food, rate of growth, and depth at which they lived.

The second phase of the study was to be done on the *Discovery* and her sister ship, the *William Scoresby*, which had joined the expedition at Capetown. This would be concerned with the environment of the whales—conditions in the ocean which determine the animal's way of life, especially the migrations. This was almost wholly oceanography, the movements of the water, changes in dissolved salts and gases, the temperatures, the life histories, the relationship of one animal group to another—in short, the chemical, physical, and biological factors in the water that affect the whales.

The first step in this long program was to find out which species of whales lived in the South Atlantic and Antarctic Oceans. Five kinds were soon discovered, the blue, fin, sei, humpback, and the sperm. With the exception of the sperm whale, Captain Ahab's foe in *Moby Dick*, all these species are toothless and are plankton eaters. (Like the sperm whale, killer whales, dolphins, and porpoises are toothed.)

The blue and fin whales constitute over ninety per cent of the catches in southern waters, the two species occurring in almost equal numbers. The blue whale, the largest living creature and perhaps the largest animal that has ever lived, and so named because of its blue-gray color, is the more valuable because it produces large quantities of oil, with an average of 70 to 80 barrels, although one produced 305 barrels.

The fin whale is smaller, more lithe, and slender (if a whale is ever lithe and slender), black above and white beneath. A curious lack of symmetry is the black whalebone plates on one side of the mouth and cream-colored plates on the other side.

The humpback, a still smaller whale that gets its name from its arched back, is black and white, so irregularly marked that no two animals are ever quite alike. In general the life history of the humpback is the same as that of the blue and fin whales, except that when krill (the usual food of whales) is not available it will eat fish and other food. Out of thirty humpbacks examined within a short time, the stomachs of six were empty, thirteen contained very little food, and the rest were crammed with fishes about the size of herring, while the stomach of one female was filled with a sticky mass of fish scales and bones.

N. J. Berrill in his book *You and the Universe* says a humpback whale needs a ton of herring in its stomach to feel comfortably full, amounting to perhaps five thousand individual fish. (How do we know when he is "comfortably full?") Continuing his discussion of the food chain, Mr. Berrill says that each herring in turn may have six or seven thousand small crustaceans in its own stomach, each of which contains one hundred and thirty thousand diatoms. "In other words, some four hundred billion yellow-green diatoms indirectly sustain a single medium sized humpback whale for a few hours at the most."

In the sperm or toothed whale the oil comes from the head cavity, but in the whalebone whales, the oil comes from the blubber, a layer of fat lying between the skin and the muscles. The quality of blubber depends upon the food supply, the season, and the animals' physical condition. Female whales are always fattest when they are pregnant and thinnest when the young are nursing, probably because the mothers are then far from their own feeding grounds, often eating nothing for months, subsisting only on the food reserve in the blubber.

Between 1927 and 1929 the production of oil from the Falkland Islands Dependencies alone was more than 2,000,000 barrels. The highest quality of oil is used for burning, candles, and soap making; the less valuable for quickening steel plates, leather dressings, softening jute and vegetable fibers; and the poorest grades for lubricants and fertilizers.

But how would one go about studying whales? Looking at the great awkward creatures bobbing up and down in the water as they came to the surface to breathe, the scientists were completely at a loss to know how or where to begin. Since whales are mammals (even as you and I), they are air breathers. To breathe, mature animals come to the surface for a brief three to six seconds, while the calves remain at the surface only two or three seconds, raising the blowhole a few inches above the surface of the water.

Like all mammals whales usually produce but one calf at a time; and they suckle their young. Even if it is possible to catch a glimpse of the whales as they dash by, they usually travel at speeds greater than that at which a boat is traveling; also the pitching and rolling of the boat tends to obscure them. Whales are continually on the move. Yet they are scattered unevenly through the water, sometimes lazing along near rich supplies of food, sometimes wandering aimlessly about.

It was well known that whales make long journeys each year, but whalers had only the vaguest notion how far or in what direction they went. They knew one was a feeding journey to the cold waters of the south in the spring; the other, a breeding one to the warm waters of the north in the late summer or autumn. Alister Hardy had no idea how far north the whales went, but he thought that their migrations might compare with those of birds which often fly from the tip of South America far into North America. Now scientists think whales never cross the equator, the northern species staying well to the north and the southern species far to the south of the equator.

The migrations of birds have been traced through banding and of fish by tagging, but almost in desperation the *Discovery* scientists wondered how one could trace the wanderings of the immense whale. They could not catch it, mark it, and send it on its way again. But some sort of marking seemed to be necessary if the range were to be studied. So it was decided to shoot from the *William Scoresby* a disk from a small shoulder gun into the blubber of the whale as it came to the surface to "blow." The disk was really a large silver-plated steel pin heavily barbed to hold it in the blubber. (Later they used a bright colored disk that could be more easily seen.) On the disk was a number, the date, the area of marking, and directions for the return of the disk to the whaling station if the animal were caught. Of course, the chances of the marked animal being caught were very slight, almost as problematic as finding a needle in the proverbial haystack, and certainly a man would have to be quick on the trigger if he were to tag the whales on the instant of the "blow."

Would the whale come close enough to the ship for the men to attempt to mark it? Would the disk be sufficiently firmly imbedded in the blubber to hold fast? Would the whale eventually be caught? And would the finder take the trouble to return the disk to the whaling station? These and dozens of other questions plagued the scientists.

Hopefully, the *William Scoresby* crew, equipped with shoulder guns and hundreds of disks, set out to outwit the whales. In two seasons the captain of the *William Scoresby* felt reasonably sure that he had marked 4,500 whales. He hoped in time that the disks would give a reliable idea of the migration of the whales. Also, in the laboratory during the first cruise of the *Discovery*, at least 2,549 whales were examined for color, external parasites (parasites are very harmful to the skin of whales), stomach content, condition of blubber, mammary and genital glands, and age.

For the capture of the whales themselves a whale catcher was employed. This is a small steamship with a low freeboard, a flared bow, and a small turning angle. An iron harpoon gun about four feet long is mounted on the bow of the platform. A powder charge fired from the gun explodes in the body of the whale, usually breaking its back. The wounded whale dives deep into the water, carrying a long stretch of rope attached to the harpoon. When at last he ceases to struggle and dies, he is hauled close to the ship where compressed air is pumped into the body to make the carcass float while being towed to the factory for stripping.

As the *Discovery* and the *William Scoresby* criss-crossed the southern seas, bit by bit the scientists learned a great many facts about the movements and the habits of these elusive animals. From information on the disk of one whale examined at the whaling station, a whaler estimated that the animal had migrated 3,000 miles from the cold Antarctic feeding grounds to the subtropical breeding area, across ten degrees of latitude. A fin whale and a blue whale recovered 2,000 miles from the place of marking had traveled at minimum speeds of 1.3 and 1.7 miles an hour. When pressed, a large blue whale can swim twenty knots and for an entire day can keep abreast of a ship making ten knots. Through scouting by airplane, a flyer was able to follow the migrations of the whales with some accuracy. (What an advancement since *Challenger* days.) Six humpbacks were known to have swum at speeds of four to seven miles an hour. A 40-foot humpback marked on July 7 off East Australia was recovered seven days later 525 miles to the north, having maintained an average speed of four miles. Assuming the migrating whales travel four to six miles an hour, they can cover the distance from the cold Antarctic to the subtropical breeding grounds in 21 to 31 days.

The whales apparently prefer specific areas for their home waters because the three species—blue, fin and humpback—were found year after year in the same part of the ocean where they had been seen and marked previously. Sometimes the herds are made up of animals of different ages, sex, and physical condition, but more often they move over great distances in groups of their own kind and sex. The humpbacks keep to much more definite rules of migration than do the blue or fin whales.

It seemed certain the migrations of the whales are closely tied up with the breeding periods, but it was impossible to be very positive about the breeding habits of whales because they are individualists and do not conform closely to definite rules in any phase of their lives. Whales become sexually mature when two years of age and females become pregnant every two years. Usually the animals mate during the summer. Almost immediately after mating they set out for the warm waters of the north where the young develops. The cow carries the calf about ten months before bearing it.

She nurses her baby like any other mammal and shows great affection for it, nuzzling it and swimming in a continuous circle around it, particularly if it is in danger. Although she usually bears a single calf, during the first *Discovery* investigation two pairs of twins were found and one whale had six foetuses. (No doubt these babies were as famous as were the Dionne quintuplets.) The mother nurses her young seven months, and during that time the baby follows her everywhere. Whales with calves trailing closely behind them were seen several times, but no one saw a calf nursing. Frequently arguments raged among the scientists as to how the young was able to hold onto the mother's teat and how it managed to take milk without it becoming mixed with salt water. However, according to one estimate the mother whale supplies her baby with a ton of very rich milk a day while lying on the surface of the sea.

Another interesting and unusual observation Alister Hardy and his men made was how whales sleep. Since they must come to the surface to breathe, when and how they slept had long been a question. These inquisitive scientists found that only rarely do they sleep at the surface. When they do, they lie motionless with their backs just below the water and their blowholes a few inches above it. More often they sleep below the water with their blowholes tightly closed, holding their breath, as it were, for an hour or two.

Of the blue whales caught on the *William Scoresby* cruises, 124 were pregnant; the smallest foetus was less than an inch and a quarter long, and the longest 25 feet. By the time the foetus is a foot and a half long, it has taken on the general shape of the adult. By the time a calf is born, it sometimes measures 20 to 25 feet and weighs more than two tons, the greatest growth and weight coming during the last two months. While nursing, the baby more than doubles its weight and length. By the time it is weaned, the calf may weight about 25 tons and may be 47 to 55 feet long. By the time the young blue whale is mature, it probably tips the scales at 88 tons. The longest blue whale ever caught measured 113.5 feet and weighed 170 tons—about one and a half tons per foot. In human terms this huge creature weighed as much as 2,276 men who averaged 150 pounds each.

After the mother has nursed her calf seven months, she sets off with her young tagging closely behind her for the cold feeding grounds a thousand miles to the south. Here the baby is weaned on *Euphausia superba,* a large shrimplike creature in the plankton called krill that is sometimes two inches long. It is hard to realize that these great monsters, far greater than the prehistoric dinosaurs, eat only one species of plankton. The dependence of the whales upon the plankton is a remarkable example of the interrelationships of the organisms in the sea. Of the several species of whales, only the sperm feeds on large animals, usually the giant squid.

To engulf the krill the whale swims along with its great mouth wide open, taking in huge gulps of water laden with myriads of krill. To separate the krill from other species of plankton, the whale forces the water out of its mouth sideways through horny baleen plates or whalebone that acts as a sieve or filter hanging from the upper jaw like a long internal mustache. The krill is caught in the whalebone filter plates. Every now and then the krill is licked off the plates by the inflated tongue and passed back to the gullet. (When women wore tight corsets, whalebone was used for the stays and was the most highly prized part of the whale, the whalebone from one animal sometimes bringing $10,000. The whalebone has now been reduced to the undistinguished position of serving as household brushes.)

The baleen plates are really exaggerations of the ridges on the roof of all mammals' mouths (even of yours and mine). In the whale they are coarse and flexible and are edged with bristles on the inner side. Strange as it may seem, the baleen plates reject everything in the water except the krill.

The life history of the krill had never been studied in detail and little or no information existed as to its relation to other animals in the plankton. Alister Hardy undertook to find out everything possible about the conditions underlying the supply of krill. He soon learned that this involved knowing the whole environment of the whales.

Unlike most animals in the plankton, which reproduce with great rapidity, the krill do not become mature for two years. During the summer the mature krill swarm in the surface waters near the edge of the ice pack often as large drifting reddish patches. While the mature animals are at the surface, the eggs become ripe and are discharged. Then both the mature and the larval animals drop down into the deep water where they spend the winter. During the winter the young krill go through at least a dozen stages of development, some genera having as many as thirty-two stages. With each stage the animal becomes more complex. With the coming of summer this new generation of krill moves up to the surface, but sinks to the deeps as the cold weather again approaches. The krill spawn the second summer after hatching.

As Alister Hardy took plankton tow after plankton tow he realized it was very patchily distributed; some areas had a great concentration of plankton, others a great scarcity. Although he dragged six plankton nets of different meshes through the water, the smallest having two hundred meshes to the square inch, it was a slow and not very efficient method of making a general survey of the plankton. To get a more comprehensive idea of the distribution and as a supplement to the tow net, Hardy constructed a machine which could be towed behind a boat at full speed at any required depth and which could sample the plankton mile after mile so as to give a continuous record of the main changes in its composition along the line of tow.

The continuous plankton recorder, as this efficient device was called, began to tell its story when a propeller turned by the passing water caused a long band of gauze to be wound around a drum as it was towed through the water. As the water passed through the gauze, it sieved out the plankton. Immediately after leaving the water tunnel the gauze was joined by another layer of gauze so that the plankton was imprisoned between them. The two layers were then automatically wound onto a storage spool. The gauze was marked into sections, each division representing one or more miles of water traversed. Each spool recorded a 250-mile run. At the end of the run, the spools were changed like the rolls on a roll-film camera. The used spools were kept for examination on a special microscope. Why hadn't he thought of using it before, Alister Hardy asked himself.

By using the continuous plankton recorder, the species, their size, and the frequency of plankton patches could be studied over a much larger area than could be done by one research ship using tow nets. If several recorders were used at the same time, it was possible to carry out surveys at different depths.

Certainly this was a much easier and more effective method of collecting plankton than was the raising and lowering of endless nets. However, even Alister Hardy was not able to devise a quick method of counting, identifying, and classifying the plankton forms. That is a statistical job that would go on for months in the laboratory with high-powered microscopes, weary brains, and tired eyes.

Never before had such an extensive plankton survey been made. Hardy's continuous plankton recorder at depths to 100 fathoms wrote a story across the southern oceans over a distance of 400 miles. As a result of surveys such as this one, Hardy felt that oceanographers will eventually be able to say—here is a plankton jungle, here a desert, and here a zone of cold water rushing in from the poles. They will also be able to predict with assurance "such and such (plankton) is in this area, in this and that season, and in this and that year." In fact he saw the distribution of life in the sea almost entirely in terms of plankton.

To show the tremendous quantities of plankton in the water and the amounts needed to feed the animals that live in the sea, Hardy cited the plankton-eating herring as an example. At least three billion herring are loaded in ports of England each year. In addition to these, many billion are brought into other ports in the North Sea. This must be but a fraction of the herring in the seas, for we know that in the long food chain the herring are the food of many marine animals. To emphasize the number of herring in the ocean, Hardy said, "If we were to imagine for a moment that these herring were land animals, sweeping in their millions across the continent, then we must imagine the whole country stripped of vegetation as by locusts."

Reducing the long food chain to its common denominator, one whale can eat as much plankton as do ten thousand herring. Instead of eating krill, as the whales do, the herring lives on copepods, no doubt the most abundant animal in the plankton. 6,500 copepods were found in the stomach of one herring. In turn the food of the copepod is the minute diatom, eating half its own weight in one day. In the English Channel half a million copepods were fished during a quarter of an hour's trawling. And so the competition for food in the seas goes on, a bigger, stronger animal always waiting to devour a smaller, weaker one. But the plankton is the basis of it all.

Our minds refuse to comprehend the fantastic numbers of plankton which must inhabit the surface waters. Besides, when we remember that the blue whale selects but one species of plankton —the krill—the problem is compounded many fold.

Near the Falkland Islands Dependencies beds of krill covered a belt extending 150 to 200 miles across the ice-free waters. In this area the temperature of the water ranged from 35° to 54° F. with the average of 48° for most of the year. Centered around a patch of krill four or five miles across, Alister Hardy saw 150 to 200 whales feeding at the same time. The krill was so thick that it formed a brick-red layer just below the surface of the water. (Who can estimate these numbers?) The krill patches were very uneven in size, varying from a few feet to those which extended in wavy lines miles in every direction.

When the whales were feeding, they cruised close to the surface blowing leisurely, and they were so preoccupied with securing their dinner that they paid no attention to the ship. Their tremendous appetites apparently being satisfied, they romped and played like children, blowing so frequently and so hard that the water looked like rocket displays. During one game they splashed the water with their heads until they raised sheets of water high into the air.

No one has devised an intelligence test for whales, but they are able to learn many things and have a highly successful communication system, including a built-in sonar system. How it works is not definitely known, but their hearing is thought to be so keen that they can send messages to one another over long distances. At the time of the first *Discovery* expedition no definite sound had been identified with them, however. Today their loud squeaks and chirps are thought to tell their fellows where to locate schools of krill.

How old do whales live to be? Judged by their enormous size, they were formerly thought to become as old as Methuselah, early guesses being 1,000 years, then 300, then 100. More recently scientists, trying to find some accurate criterion of age, sought the answer in ridges in the baleen plates or in parasite wounds in the skin. Neither of these gave a reliable clue to their age. A *Discovery* scientist completely upset the notion that whales are long lived by saying those he examined at the South Georgia whaling station were, he believed, only six or seven years old, certainly not over ten. And that was all the *Discovery* scientists would say about the age of whales. The editors of *Life*'s book *The Sea* say that blue whales live at least fifty years.

For two years the men of the *Discovery* worked from dawn to dark studying the habits and life history of the great ugly whales. (There was no overtime pay on a whale ship.) Finally the ship was beginning to show her age, and battered by wind and tide she needed repairs. The men too needed the comforts of civilization, so the ship returned to England laden with so much material that it took five years to analyze it.

In spite of the achievements of the *Discovery* scientists, everyone realized that scarcely a dent had been made in the study of the South Atlantic and Antarctic waters. The scope of the work was so far reaching that everyone agreed the work should be continued, so a new vessel, *Discovery II*, was planned to help her older sister.

To the great disappointment of his shipmates and the scientists of England, Alister Hardy left the *Discovery* to accept a university professorship, which has brought him the highest academic honors. He assured his associates that his new post did not mean he would merely sit in a college office or lecture to young students for the rest of his life. Nothing could keep him from the sea he loves so deeply. And so it has been. Since 1945 he has been Professor of Zoology at Oxford, but scarcely a summer has passed that, dressed in dungarees and boots, he was not back on the tossing seas dredging, studying plankton and fish, and sketching sea life.

Over the years Alister Hardy, now Sir Alister, has written widely and beautifully about the nature and adaptations of marine animals to their environment. A remarkable gift is his ability to describe unfamiliar animals and involved scientific procedures to the layman in an informal, interesting, almost humorous style.

In 1954, while reading proof for his book *The Open Sea,* Sir Alister sat on the deck of *Discovery II* scanning the contents of each haul as it was dumped on the deck and sketching new and rare creatures before their brilliant colors faded. When he began the book, he intended to write a natural history of the sea apart from the birds and the seashore. He soon realized he could not do justice to the subject in one volume. So he wrote two, *The Open Sea,* with the subtitle "The World of Plankton," published in 1956, and *The Open Sea,* with the subtitle "Fish and Fisheries," published in 1958.

By 1929 the new *Discovery II* was finished and was ready to begin her long journey to the Antarctic under the direction of G. E. R. Deacon. She was less beautiful than her famous namesake, but she was equipped as no other oceanographic ship had been outfitted for marine study. Ever since 1602 the name *Discovery* has been linked with British exploration. Between that early date and 1860 seven vessels had been named *Discovery.* And since the beginning of the twentieth century two more have been so named, Scott's famous old ship and the new *Discovery II.* Most of the work of *Discovery I* and *II* has been carried on in the southern seas. Even today, scarcely a year passes without a report of the findings of *Discovery II,* and it can truthfully be said that, with the possible exception of the *Challenger,* no ships have made such a great contribution to ocean study.

The 1929–1930 expeditions of *Discovery II* were sponsored by Great Britain, Australia, and New Zealand for exploration of the totally uncharted coastline between Gaussberg and Coats Land, an area stretching across more than 100 degrees of longitude in the Indian Ocean. In a century no part of that coastline had been seen by Europeans. No doubt the lack of interest in this area can be explained in part because in latitudes near the Antarctic Circle terrific storms rage. Everywhere are huge ice blocks, some "as big as football fields," which rise to heights of eighty feet. In some areas mountains of ice moved nearly 400 miles beyond the ice ledge. At one place 192 bergs could be seen drifting across the water at the same time. For several weeks *Discovery II* worked in the shadow of a berg fifty feet tall. Fortunately, even in the ice pack the temperature was moderate, rarely falling below 28° F. Bergs or no bergs, a continuous and systematic examination of the plankton was kept. Because the bergs interfered with the continuous plankton recorder, special nets were built to fish below the ice.

The difficulty of bringing plankton nets up from between the blocks of ice was partly overcome by shooting the gear while the ship was slowly turning to port. This opened up a broad lane or pool behind the ship and the ice floe did not close as readily as when the ship followed a straight course. To avoid catching the ice fragments, the nets closed just before they were raised from the water. As one can imagine, surveying in ice-infested water took much time and infinite patience.

A part of the 1929–1930 cruise of the ship was not strictly an investigation of the sea. But in a completely uncharted region it was hard to know what was of first importance. To supply much needed information on the upper air movements south of Australia, the scientists used airplanes and released thirty-four pilot balloons, which recorded the direction and velocity of the winds to a height of 53,000 feet.

The story is endless. Yet through never-ending toil these dedicated men wrested from Father Neptune the secrets he had always guarded so closely. It is impossible to enumerate all the ship's achievements. The avowed purpose of the early expeditions of this research ship was to furnish a basis for a rational regulation of the whaling industry, in other words to tell the whalers how far they could go. And this they did, thus fitting into place another piece of the jigsaw puzzle.

Faithfully the *Discovery I* and *II*, the *William Scoresby*, the biological laboratory, the whale catchers, and the whaling station amassed mountains of facts about every phase of the life of the whale and set up regulations for the industry under the British Colonial Office. Yet in the Antarctic during the past fifty years whalers operating factory ships have killed over one million whales. The blue whales are now so few that it is difficult for them to find mates in the great ocean. But far and above the contribution to the knowledge of whales, the many expeditions of the *Discovery* opened up the whole Antarctic to scientific study and instituted improved methods of research until long programs of sounding, trawling, temperature readings, plankton studies, chemical analyses, and all the other tests could be taken with almost machine-like precision.

To the crew and ship's officers the work was no doubt dull and routine, but the scientists felt a tremendous sense of achievement in having had a part in contributing to the understanding of this little known part of the seas. Particularly were they rewarded when they saw the echo sounder charting a course across the ocean floor with almost the same precision that surveyors plan a highway across the mountains or when the continuous plankton recorder revealed areas of plenty or scarcity. The use of airplanes for scouting in the ice-bound seas and the sending up of balloons promised a new era in polar meteorological research.

The intensive examination of the krill focused man's attention upon the limitless food resources of the sea. (Already a number of studies are being made on the possibility of using plankton and seaweed as food for man.) Above all, the spirit of adventure and devotion that drove these men to endure the dangers and hardships of the frozen seas will always mark them as torch bearers in the great drama of scientific research.

Sir Alister Hardy once remarked, "The difficulties add spice to the game. A golf course would indeed be dull if there were no bunkers in it."

✿ ✿ ✿

Determined to turn back the pages of the earth's history books, Hans Pettersson, a Swedish oceanographer, found records dating back 3,000,000 years by boring into the sediments that lie on the floor of the ocean.

8

Hans Pettersson —
The Albatross

Any man who goes to sea for pleasure would go to hell for a pastime.

One evening in 1910 after listening to a lecture given by Sir John Murray, that grand old man of research, Hans Pettersson, a young Swedish scientist, said to a friend, "Of course the past is the key to the present."

Murray had told that during the *Challenger* Expedition he had stamped out sediment cores one or two feet in length from the bottom of the ocean. Murray had prophesied that borings such as these would in the future reveal undreamed of facts about the early history of the planet that had been locked away far below the earth for millions of years.

At that moment there flashed into Hans Pettersson's mind the idea of sometime sponsoring a round-the-world Swedish Deep Sea Expedition on which he would learn to read the early chapters of this ancient history book. At that time Hans Pettersson was a student at University College in London, so the possibilities of realizing such an ambition seemed very remote, but he never lost the dream.

Only a man like Hans Pettersson, who had lived all his life on the windswept shores of the Skagerak, an arm of the North Sea between Norway and Denmark, and who passionately loved the ocean, would probably be interested in ferreting out this age-old story.

For many generations Hans Pettersson's family had lived in a wooden house called "Kalhuvudet" which in Swedish means "head of cabbage," so named from the shape of the rock on which the house was built. In order to withstand the fiercest onslaughts of the wind and storms, the house had thick walls and tiny windows. On stormy nights the winds pressed against the old timbers making the walls creak and sigh in protest against the elements and the rigors of the north.

In the house was quaint old furniture salvaged from ships that had been wrecked on the nearby rocky shores. The house lay so close to the water that Pettersson told that once during the Napoleonic wars a ship rammed right into the house. The captain and his wife, with a baby in her ams, had stepped directly from the boat into the house through the kitchen window. From the house at night the Petterssons could watch the beams of the Pater Noster Lighthouse sweeping across the surrounding waters as a reminder to the local families to say prayers for themselves and their men far out at sea.

"With such an ancestry and such an environment, the sea is bound to become an obsession," wrote Pettersson as he tried to explain his love of the north and his desire to find out more about the great oceans of the world.

In his laboratory overlooking the Baltic, Hans' father, Otto Pettersson, a well-known oceanographer, had for many years studied the tides as they rolled in and out of his fiord. At the advanced age of ninety-three the old gentleman was still intensely desirous of studying life both in the heavens and in the sea. On the very day of his death he was still setting up his instruments and making calculations on the moving waters. Only a few days earlier he had said to his son, "What will sustain me in my last moments will be an infinite curiosity as to what is to follow."

Hans had always planned to carry on the work of his father, but, after his meeting with John Murray, his sights were extended far beyond the narrow confines of the Skagerak. After taking a Doctor of Science degree at the University of Stockholm, and studying at Upsala University and the University College in London, Pettersson returned to the Skagerak to ponder the layers of water, the submarine waves, and the currents along the coasts of Sweden. From 1923 to 1928 he led a team of workers at the Institute of Radium Treatment in Vienna. Yet he had never forgotten what Sir John Murray had said about the sediments that lay beneath the ocean floor.

In the early 1930's Pettersson was appointed Professor of Oceanography in the University of Göteborg. He decided that the time was now ripe to enlist the interest of the people of Sweden in a deep sea expedition, one worthy of the great sea power Sweden had always been.

He talked to everyone he met about the wonderful possibilities of learning the geological history of the earth through boring deep into the sediments on the ocean floor, emphasizing that Sweden should be a pioneer in this great study. To arouse interest in the idea, he made radio broadcasts, wrote articles for the press, gave lectures, and wrote books. He appealed also to the wealthy men of Göteborg for financial help, for he knew they had always been generous to the arts and sciences. On the other hand Pettersson was realistic enough to know that an expedition such as he planned was a very costly thing, a well-equipped ship even more costly, and a highly trained staff still more difficult to assemble.

Then came World War II, which kept the Scandinavians from their beloved sea. However, during this time the Göteborg scientists were far from idle. In fact their isolation gave them a good deal of time to engage in research, especially in the construction of instruments for deep sea study, and to convince the people of the part Sweden should play in the exploration of the seas.

In 1945 the war was over. Hans Pettersson had prepared his campaign so well that almost as soon as the guns were stilled at the close of the war, the Brostrom Shipping Company offered him the use of their training ship, the *Albatross,* a combined sailing and steam vessel of 1,540 tons, for a fifteen-month round-the-world cruise. From the Royal Society of Göteborg and a number of other generous donors came money for equipment and operation of the ship. As the result of the cooperation of these sea-loving citizens, the first Swedish round-the-world deep sea expedition was financed without any help from the government.

When Professor Pettersson was chosen leader of the project, he was the happiest man in the world. His dream of thirty years was about to come true. He did not waste a minute. Almost immediately he made a trial run with the *Skagerak* to the Mediterranean to test the instruments that they had worked so hard to perfect. These having proved efficient, he drafted the itinerary of the *Albatross*— the North Atlantic, the Caribbean Sea, the Panama Canal into the Pacific, the South Sea islands, the Indian Ocean, the Red Sea, and finally the Mediterranean and back to Göteborg.

Because of the heavy gear needed to operate their new instruments, especially the depth corer and the echo sounder, and their great cost, it was decided that the *Albatross* should stay within latitudes of 30° North and 30° South, the tropics, where heavy seas and stormswept waters were rare. Too, the ocean floor near the equator, between depths of 2,000 to 3,000 fathoms, was favorable for the work of the *Albatross*. Another advantage of working in tropical waters was that the region had not been extensively studied. Of course, the primary object of the voyage was to take sediment cores, strata lying one above the other like a many layered cake, and through them to estimate the age of the deposit and thus to find out the biological and geological conditions of the earth at the time the sediments were laid down. This would include a survey of the bottom of the sea at all depths, the type of deposits found, their interaction with the ocean waters, and the thickness of the sediment carpet.

At the same time the scientists would make a study of the water layers from surface to bottom, the temperature and salinity, the amount of dissolved oxygen, the nutrient salts, and the general biological conditions of the ocean. As a corollary to these jobs, the scientists would investigate the radioactive elements—radium and uranium—in the water. Pettersson believed that these timekeepers of the world might be of help in calculating the age of different strata and their rate of settling.

The idea of taking sediment cores was not new. Ever since the days of the *Challenger* Expedition, when John Murray had stamped out cores a couple of feet long, attempts had been made to take samples of underwater sediments. Forty years later the German Atlantic Expedition ship, the *Meteor*, obtained three-foot samples. In the early 1900's C. S. Piggott of Carnegie Institute used an explosive sampler that shot the coring tube down into the deposit from a kind of submarine gun that automatically discharged on contact with the bottom. This brought up undisturbed samples of from five to ten feet.

These cores read like newspaper accounts of glacial deposits laid down when the surface of the earth was cooled by drifting ice floes and icebergs. One of Piggott's cores showed two layers of volcanic ash laid down about 3,000 years ago, lying on top of the glacial deposits. With their new tools the *Albatross* scientists hoped to penetrate much farther back into history.

By the 1940's almost everyone knew that, in the millions of years since the surface of the earth had hardened, great upheavals had taken place within the planet. Continents and islands and mountains had been hurled up and torn down by volcanoes, earthquakes, and rushing waters. Through such records geologists had been able to piece together a good deal of information about the history of the earth's surface. However, many of the surface records had been obliterated by erosion, rains, and winds, leaving frequent blank or torn pages in the ancient geological textbooks.

Professor Pettersson believed that the record was much more complete in the deep sea than on the earth's surface. Here the deposits had never, or at least rarely, been changed and, therefore, they represented hundreds of thousands of years of undisturbed history. The deposits had been formed by the incessant fall from the surface of foraminifera and other plankton forms; of volcanic ash; of meteors; and of all kinds of donations from the earth. Together these formed a deep carpet over the ocean floor. It was these sediment deposits that Hans Pettersson was eager to investigate.

As soon as the formalities concerning the use of the *Albatross* had been worked out, Professor Pettersson began to prepare the ship for her great adventure. Air-conditioned cabins for a staff of ten, laboratories, low-temperature storage rooms, facilities for handling heavy gear, and a well-stocked galley were provided. The crew, including Professor Pettersson's young son, were like boys on a holiday.

Amid tremendous excitement the *Albatross* slipped out of the harbor of Göteborg July 4, 1947. The beautiful white ship, gallantly riding the sunlit waters with her sails in full array, was saluted by whistles, sirens, flags, and shouts. Celebrities, donors—big and little —stood proudly by. On board the men were in a hilarious mood, for they were sure that the sea had been waiting for millions of years to tell them a wonderful tale of bygone ages.

These fair-haired Swedes, overjoyed to get away for a short time from the North and the restrictions of the war years, began dreaming of the bright blue waters of the tropics, waving palms, exotic flowers, dazzling white beaches, and dancing girls. But beneath the gaiety was deep concern that their brave plans and newly designed instruments would turn back the pages of geological history. The whole idea of a deep drilling such as Pettersson planned was still experimental and, even if long cores could be secured, would the scientists be able to interpret the records of the past as written in the vertical layers of sediment far below the ocean floor?

The second day out of Göteborg the sea became angry and rough. The waving palms and the dancing girls were forgotten. The sky was leaden, the wind howled and tore at the ship's sails. The men sought the ship's rail, then went to bed. The storm persisted through the Skagerak, the North Sea, and the English Channel, slowing the ship to a mere crawl. With 40,000 miles to travel in fifteen months, Hans Pettersson was maddened by this snail's pace and the listless men.

But even a head wind does not last forever. By the time the ship reached the Bay of Biscay, the elements were peaceful and the men gay. Borja Kullenberg could hardly wait to try his new piston core sampler through which he hoped to obtain undisturbed sediment columns of perhaps sixty or seventy feet.

To test the corer the ship was headed into the wind and held as immobile as possible by the engine. The corer, a long steel cylinder with a piston inside, was operated by water pressure. Lifted from its horizontal position on the deck by an electric winch, the weighted corer was lowered rapidly into the water. Down it went. The moment the corer reached the floor, it was plunged into the sediment. The piston inside the coring tube remained stationary in contact with the sediment while the heavy corer descended, forcing a column of sediment upward inside the piston.

But sad to say on the first attempt at coring, Kullenberg's piston tube came up empty. Incredible. What had happened? Its inventor was terribly disappointed. The next day he tried to drive the corer into the sediment by exploding a charge of dynamite. Again there was no indication of a sediment carpet. What could be the trouble?

The only explanation Dr. Kullenberg could offer was that there was no sediment in that area, that strong tides had swept the bed rock clean of sediment, or that the corer had struck a layer of basalt recently laid down by a submarine volcano. The Swedes soon learned that disappointments and impossible-to-explain conditions are the daily lot of oceanographers. They also learned that work in the great open oceans was much more difficult than in the protected fiords of Sweden.

Since the sediment corer was a very costly instrument, Professor Pettersson could not take chances on its being lost or broken, for the success or failure of the expedition depended upon it. Thereafter the echo sounder acted as a scout by drawing a detailed picture of the ocean floor before a coring was attempted.

With the echo sounder making preliminary surveys of the ocean floor, a number of successful cores of 20 to 60 feet were taken near the Central Atlantic Ridge, representing a time span of 3,000,000 years. The echo sounder, a marvel of engineering, draws a continuous and precise picture in ink of the sea bottom thousands of feet below the ship's keel.

Professor Pettersson gives a detailed description of this amazing instrument by saying,

Far down in the hull of the ship is a bundle of nickel plates vibrating 10,000 times per second under the influence of a strong magnetic field varying with the same frequency. Short pulses of these ultrasonic waves concentrated downwards by a reflector behind the vibrator are passing through a thin steel membrane, reaching an electric receiver. From there the supersonic waves are transformed into electric impulses, conducted to the echograph in the laboratory. The moment between the giving off and the reception of the pulses is recorded on a chemically treated strip of paper slowly rotated by an electric motor. From a sequence of small dots a curve appears showing how the bottom rises and falls along the course the ship is following.

Sound waves in the water travel 5,000 feet per second, so it is easy to determine the depth by multiplying the echo time by 5,000 to find the total distance that the ultrasonic impulses have traveled, which is twice the actual depth. The echo sounder measures the ups and downs of the ocean bottom in a fraction of a second, whereas by using the older method of attaching a lead to a steel wire each sounding took several hours.

If the echo sounder showed the bottom was fairly level and covered with sediment, Kullenberg sent the corer down as deeply as possible, and the sediment rose in the piston, being held there by a device called a core catcher, which prevented the sediment from dropping out of the piston. As soon as the winch raised the load to the deck, twenty-eight inch sections of the lining tube were pushed out of the steel tube, stored in plastic, and enclosed in aluminum tubes. The sections were then taken to the cold storage room where they were packed to await detailed study in Göteborg. The cores from a depth of 3,500 fathoms taken in the Atlantic were a chocolate brown, indicative of ancient red clay, while those taken from 1,500 fathoms were almost white, characteristic of more recent globigerina ooze.

The next step in taking a sediment core was measuring the thickness of the sediment carpet at the point where the core was taken. This was done by dropping a charge of dynamite.

Following the explosion, strong echoes are thrown back against the upper sediment surface while much fainter echoes are reflected against the lower surface of the sediment carpet after the explosion wave has twice traveled through the whole thickness. Since the velocity of sound is five times higher in water than in air, the time lag between the upper and lower echoes affords a means of calculating the thickness of the reflecting layer.

By applying this complicated system of echoes, the scientists estimated the sediment in the Atlantic extended 12,000 feet below the floor itself. If the thickness of the carpet is uniform throughout the area and if the red clay sediment has accumulated at the rate of one-fourth inch in a thousand years, it has taken 500,000,000 years for the 12,000 feet of sediment to settle.

However, the professor had reason to believe the lower layers of sediment are more closely packed than the upper layers and therefore they have accumulated more slowly, making the total time of settling of the red clay longer than 500,000,000 years. Near the West Indies the *Albatross* stamped out seventy-foot cores, the longest taken, representing a time spance of at least 3,000,000 years.

As the *Albatross* sped across the Atlantic at eight or nine knots, Pettersson noticed that the big winch was slightly bent, so he decided to run into Funchal on Madeira Island for repairs. Enroute to the island the echo sounder "saw" an enormous range of mountains stretching hundreds of miles in a north-south direction. The peaks of the mountains were so tall and thin that only recently had they been discovered, and then quite by accident while cables were being laid across the ocean.

Three of these skyscrapers were as high as the Andes or the Alps, their summits reaching so near the surface ships could be anchored on them in the open sea, while just beyond them were dizzying cliffs and plunging canyons, low hills and hummocks, and sometimes the floor was almost a level plain.

For several hours before reaching Madeira, Hans Pettersson watched the echo sounder recording this highly dramatic picture of submerged peaks that he felt sure had been spewed up as red hot lava eons ago. One of the peaks had burst through the surface of the water to form Madeira, standing 6,000 feet above the water—monarch of all it surveyed. Gleaming in the morning sun, the island was to Hans Pettersson "a roseate dream floating on a sea of lapis lazuli."

After weeks of confinement, strict discipline, and hard work on the ship some of the men were wondering if perhaps Samuel Johnson was not right when he said, "Any man who goes to sea for pleasure would go to hell for a pastime." But the men's brief stay on the Emerald Isle of the Atlantic restored their spirits, for the island was to them pure joy—the flowers, the dancing girls of whom they had dreamed back in Sweden, the carefree life.

The Swedes were especially intrigued by the making and the tasting of the famous Madeira wines prized in Europe since Elizabethan days. But Professor Pettersson, driven by the time clock, could not linger long on the island.

Her white sails billowing, on hurried the *Albatross* toward the West Indies. In the early dawn, as he rested on the deck with his son beside him, Hans Pettersson watched the sun rising above the horizon, the gleaming blue water, the flying fish, "Those glittering dragon-flies of the sea skimming in and out of the water by vibrating their tail fins." At the same time he did not forget the hardworking echo sounder busily photographing the underseas landscape. The remarkable ruggedness of the deep ocean floor and the islands which the volcanic eruptions have produced are beautiful to behold, but they also present many dangers.

The islands rest upon a great fold in the earth's crust which puts them under tremendous strain of earthquakes and volcanic eruptions. One of the worst outbursts in modern times occurred on Martinique in 1902 when the peak of Mount Pelée was completely blown off in a mighty explosion. The eruption was so gigantic that a river of red lava, sweeping down the sides of the mountain, completely wiped out the city of St. Pierre and its 28,000 inhabitants.

During their brief stay on the island, the *Albatross* scientists forgot the earthquakes and the volcanoes. They were as enchanted by the marvelous scenery, the exotic flowers, the gleaming white beaches, and the gaiety of the people as Robert Louis Stevenson and Herman Melville had been long before. Several men of the *Albatross* made an excursion to the weird volcanic rocks near the crater of Mount Pelée, where a thick curtain of fog formed a somber, almost frightening background for the bright hibiscus and bougainvillaea blossoms.

Again, in the Panama Canal Zone, the seamen welcomed a breakdown of the ship's equipment, for it meant a reprieve from the routine of the ship. It also meant dancing and laughter. Yet Hans Pettersson never let the crew forget that they were embarked on a very serious expedition. After passing through the canal the *Albatross* with its snow-white hull and fullblown sails continued to head west toward the fabled Pacific Isles—Galapagos, the enchanted; Tahiti, the queen of the South Seas; Hawaii, the pearl of the Pacific; the Gilberts, King David's Isle; Samoa, the isle of jewels; and all the others.

Through the 20,000,000 or 30,000,000 years of their existence, these islands, like the West Indies, have suffered many disasters. They are constantly rocked by the terrific turmoil within the earth—submarine fissures, raging fires, gigantic earthquakes, and white-hot lava flows. Volcanic cones have been built up, one upon another; islands have been born, then as regularly torn down.

Toward the northern edge of this island chain lie the Hawaiian Islands. Like their neighbors these islands were formed through volcanic eruptions. A few of the mountains, like Mauna Loa and Mauna Kea, are still intermittently active. One of the early European visitors to these islands was Captain James Cook, who, in 1775, was so enchanted with their beauty that he called them the "crown jewels of the Pacific." Captain Cook named these far-flung jewels the Sandwich Islands in honor of his patron, the Earl of Sandwich, the First Lord of the British Admiralty.

Now nearly a hundred and seventy-five years later, as the *Albatross* approached Honolulu, Hans Pettersson and his men were as impressed with the beauty of the islands as Captain Cook had been, but fortunately their welcome was far more cordial. (Captain Cook was killed on a visit there.) As a greeting to the *Albatross*, airplanes swooped down like seagulls, photographers, officials, and the melting pot of its citizenry overwhelmed them with music, leis, and luaus. Loveliness was on every side.

Everywhere throughout the Pacific were islands crowned with dazzling white coral on which waved graceful palm trees. Yet the *Albatross* scientists asked, as men had done for centuries, what great cataclysm had formed the Pacific, the largest and deepest of the oceans. Professor Kullenberg believed this to be one of the great unsolved puzzles of our planet.

Some people think that the great ocean was gouged out when the moon was torn from the body of the earth by a huge wave raised by the sun some 300,000,000 years ago. Others believe that the immense basin was formed by internal forces that shaped and reshaped the earth's contours. Within the great body of water land has been raised up and torn down many times until at the present time far out in the Pacific is a chain of islands so close together they no doubt formed at one time a series of land bridges extending from the fog-bound Aleutians to the sunny South Sea isles of Fiji and Tonga.

Although today they are peaceful islands, just beyond them lie the deepest troughs and trenches in the ocean, a reminder of an ever-present threat of new turbulence. There is not complete agreement among scientists as to the origin of these trenches, but no doubt they were formed by the great tensions built up between these land bridges and the deeps that not only cause earth tremors but are responsible for seismic waves that race through the ocean at speeds of more than a thousand feet per second, often causing havoc in places half the world away.

Biologists as well as geologists have been interested in whether these islands were once connected. If it could be proved that land bridges actually existed, it would do much to explain how wingless insects, plants, and other land forms were able to spread from island to island, far removed from one another.

On such questions Professor Pettersson pondered long and hard. His conclusion was that they could be solved only if geophysicists, geologists, and oceanographers work closely together, for many of their problems are so intimately linked that it is impossible to say where one begins and the other leaves off. He hoped that the new techniques of coring might throw some light on the complex matter of land bridges.

In some ways coring in the Pacific was somewhat disappointing, for the sediment cores here did not indicate that the material had come from so early a period as it had done in the Atlantic. This could no doubt be explained by the fact that volcanic fires had spread over large areas of the Pacific ocean floor, leaving layers of lava lying atop layers of sediment one above the other. In other places the lava was so evenly spread that the height of the floor did not vary more than a few fathoms. Nowhere west of the Galapagos Islands were echoes recorded as coming from depths greater than 1,000 fathoms, indicating that the sediment did not extend below that depth or that it was entirely covered by later lava flows.

That the lava acted as a reflecting surface that blocked the echo was confirmed when a number of times broken fragments of lava were found in the bit of the corer.

The Pacific is an ocean of contrasts. After sailing for several days over almost perfectly level areas, without warning the echo sounder began to report an abrupt drop in the ocean floor, until finally in the Mindanao Trench it registered a depth of 5,000 fathoms or 30,000 feet. The Challenger Deep near Guam was even deeper. In fact it is 37,000 feet or seven miles below the water's surface, the deepest known hole in the earth. (The Bathyscaph found it to be 37,800 feet.) It is so deep that the time interval required to transmit sound waves from this depth back to the receiving hydrophones on shipboard is 14 seconds.

Much as the *Albatross* scientists would have liked to attempt corings at this great depth, they knew their equipment was not equal to it, so Kullenberg contented himself with taking a number of soundings in the Emden Deep at 5,100 fathoms. The deepest coring he attempted was at 4,300 fathoms, but unfortunately the cable snapped and the precious corer was lost after penetrating but eight feet into the sediment surface. To the men's great disappointment they took home no sediment samples from the great depths.

Instead they took water samples from the trenches for analyses of radium and uranium.

Several times, while in the area of the great deeps the ship narrowly escaped the playground of the typhoons. The most frightening experience was an encounter with winds and 25-foot waves that rocked the ship up and down at a 35° angle. After more than five weeks on the high seas, the *Albatross* headed for Ternate, a small volcanic island in the Moluccan group, famous since before Magellan's time for its spices. In Ternate the men would have a well-earned rest. On an oceanography ship the men often work the clock around. They consider themselves lucky if they can occasionally snatch a few hours' rest on the bowsprit gazing at the shooting stars, the Southern Cross, or marveling at the tiny living lights in the waters below.

When the ship arrived at Ternate, Professor Pettersson found that it was ruled by a sultan of a very ancient dynasty (with a Dutch counselor always at his side). The Sultan welcomed the Swedes very cordially and served them a royal banquet of thirty-five courses; and still he apologized for the frugal meal. (Before the war seventy courses were offered on a festive occasion.)

The journey from Ternate to Bali was slowed up by strong currents, rough seas, and high winds, but Bali, the crown jewel of the fairy island group, was so delightful that it made up for the discomforts of the surrounding seas. As the ship approached the land, it moved through the blue seas that glittered in the sunshine by day and in moonlight by night, the surface broken only by flying fish playing around the bow of the ship.

The men were completely carried away by the beauty of this fabled island—the palm trees, the flowers, the coral beaches—but it was the happy, hospitable people that captivated everyone from the lowliest seaman to Captain Krafft and Professor Pettersson, who called Bali "the last refuge of beauty in a ruined world." Yet he was realistic enough to see another side of the gaiety and was reminded of the quotation, "The palm thrives, the coral grows, but man dies."

The young seamen were so bewitched by the rhythm and the syncopation of the music and by the romance of the tropics that several of them deserted the ship to remain in Paradise. Not only in Bali did the hospitality and the romantic atmosphere turn the heads of these young Swedes, but everywhere they went was the same charm and the same beauty—Tahiti, Fiji, the Marquesas (although this island was made memorable by a violent earthquake).

But time was passing and work was pressing. So the *Albatross* hurried toward the Indian Ocean. The history of this ocean is still uncertain, but geologists all agree that it is by far the youngest of the oceans, probably less than a million years old. (A detailed study of the Indian Ocean is now being made.) According to many earth scientists, an enormous continent once linked East Africa with Arabia, India, and Australia. The theory is given credence by a strong similarity between the plant and animal fossils in these great land masses. In some far-off time a violent catastrophe may have broken these islands apart, submerging great areas. Yet today submarine ridges, many of them lying above the surface as islands and running in a north-south direction, are thought to be remnants of the lost continent.

Although Hans Pettersson hoped his cores would reveal something of the nature of the submarine ridges, he was not able to turn back the pages of history fifty or seventy million years since the continent disappeared beneath the sea. The deepest core from the Indian Ocean was only 25 feet, composed of very compact layers of sediment varying from nearly white to black, interspersed with green mixed with layers of globigerina ooze.

Much as the Swedes hated leaving the warm, sunny lands so different from their cold bleak north, Captain Krafft, determined to be back in Göteborg by the time the ship's lease expired, reluctantly turned the ship homeward in the early spring of 1948, after crossing the equator thirteen times, by traveling through the Red Sea and into the Mediterranean. This ancient inland sea had always been considered an ideal area for submarine study. The weather is usually fair, the swell of the water moderate, the visibility excellent, and the depths within each reach of harbors.

Now, as it had so often done, the Mediterranean generously offered its gifts of the sea to the Scandinavians, and the men of the *Albatross* made good use of its riches. Especially in the Tyrrhenian Sea to a much greater degree than in the Pacific the sediment cores could be correlated with the early known history of the earth. The sediment was largely of volcanic origin that corresponded closely to eruptions of Mount Vesuvius.

The increasing number and thickness of ash layers toward the lower end of the core indicated more frequent volcanic eruptions in the past than at present. For example, the strata in cores taken at 2,000 fathoms told in detail of the terrific explosion of Vesuvius in 79 A.D. which buried Pompeii and Herculaneum. Sediment from lower strata in the cores seemed to agree with the eruption of Santorin north of Crete in 1600 B.C., which destroyed much of the island and caused great disturbance in the ocean.

In *Westward Ho with the Albatross* Professor Pettersson suggests that clouds of ash thrown up by that eruption might have been carried across the Mediterranean to Egypt by the prevailing winds and could have been responsible for the "Egyptian darkness" which the Bible lists as the ninth plague that smote Pharaoh when the Lord was trying to persuade him to release the children of Israel from bondage. In Exodus 10:21 we read, "And the Lord said unto Moses, 'Stretch out thine hand toward Heaven that there may be darkness over the land of Egypt, even darkness which can be felt.' "

Professor Pettersson says that these ash clouds seem to confirm the rather hazy chronology of the Old Testament that tells that when fierce winds swept across the desert they turned day into night; they burned and blinded; and the sands were so harsh they could be felt. The ash rains, which archeologists place about 1600 B.C., the time of this eruption, correspond to an estimated eight or ten inches of sediment laid down in a thousand years (a great thickness for a thousand years).

The longest cores that the *Albatross* took in the Mediterranean between Malta and Sicily were sixty feet. In all, the *Albatross* brought home more than 250 cores samples that if laid end to end would extend more than a mile. Much has been written about them, but in 1953, when Professor Pettersson wrote *Westward Ho with the Albatross,* he felt that not enough detailed study has been given the cores as yet to say with any certainty what they revealed.

For some years radium and other radioactive elements had been used in studying the timetable on land. Now Hans Pettersson was eager to study the amount of radium in deep sea water. The discovery of radium by Madame Curie in the last decade of the nineteenth century had been responsible for tremendous changes in the basic concepts in physics, chemistry, astronomy, and geophysics. The enormous energy set free by radioactive substances "explained how the stars generate their stupendous torrents of radiant energy," and told fabulous stories of rocks being solidified from a molten state

2,000,000,000 years ago, and of the earth being formed a billion years before that.

Scientists knew that radioactive elements are much more abundant in the earth's outer crust than in deeper strata. To verify or deny this in the underseas sediments, Professor Pettersson checked cores from the deep red clay for radium, but the deeper he probed the less radium he found. A layer of undersea sediment approximately 10,000 years old contained a considerable amount of radium, while sediments 80,000 years old showed only fifty per cent as much as the 10,000 year sediment, and at 160,000 years only twenty-five per cent as much.

Using this rate of radioactive disintegration as a norm, Professor Pettersson believed that it should not be difficult to find the age of different strata below the water. Yet he realized that so many factors may disturb the distribution of radium in a core, it is impossible to give an exact estimate of it. All he would say with any certainty was that at present there seemed no hope of obtaining usable quantities of radioactive elements from the depth of the sea.

Another exciting technique used in deep sea research on the *Albatross* was reading the past by the pollen-analytical method. Many sediment cores from the Tyrrhenian Sea contained perfectly preserved pollen grains from trees, shrubs, and trailing plants although they may have been buried millions of years. Microscopic examinations of the cores showed recognizable pollen grains, from evergreen forests in Italy and Sardinia, which had been carried out to sea. Certainly, if evergreens once grew in these countries, they have undergone great climatic changes through the centuries.

Because the *Albatross* was the first ship in the Mediterranean to make pollen-analytical analyses, there was no pollen key (a systematic classification of the characteristics of the members of a plant group that makes identification easier) that was valid for these coasts, so no definite conclusions could be drawn. Since deep sea cores containing pollen grains were first studied, they have been used many times to date a certain layer of vegetation from the relative frequency of the different pollen grains found in it. In the Mediterranean waters the sediment cores were rich both in pollen grains and in other coastal vegetation.

We turn the pages of the ancient history book backward until we come to what Hans Pettersson believed was the opening chapter of the story of deep sea sediments. This tells about the meteors and meteoric dust buried deep in the ocean. Small droplets of molten nickel-iron from outer space have apparently bombarded the earth since the beginning of time until the floor of the ocean has become the burial ground of countless burned-out meteors, where they look like dirty potatoes. No doubt it was huge meteors which pockmarked the moon and left great craters upon it.

Even today scarcely a night passes that streaks of light are not seen sweeping across the sky. Shooting stars we call them. From somewhere off in space a meteor has penetrated the top layers of our atmosphere, 50 to 100 miles overhead. Most of them burn out before they reach the earth or the oceans, but occasionally a nickel-alloy meteor reaches the ground where it causes great excitement, and naturally so, for meteors are the only matter from outside the earth's atmosphere to reach the earth.

Our old friend John Murray was probably the first oceanographer to interest himself in these metallic spheres. While on the *Challenger* he dredged up in the globigerina ooze a number of metal balls, some of them less than one-hundredth of an inch in diameter. Not much thought was given to them until a professor in Dublin began analyzing them for radium and its disintegration product, helium. His tests showed they may be thousands of million years old.

Between Tahiti and Hawaii Professor Pettersson had raised many metal balls from great depths. On land they are very rare, but in the ocean they form a considerable part of the ancient red clay sediment. Trying to follow up every possible clue to the rate of sedimentation, Hans Pettersson wondered whether the number of metallic spheres per unit of sediment might serve as a possible answer to this question of the age of deposits.

In *Between the Planets* a Harvard researcher stated that over ten million foreign bodies may enter our atmosphere each day. This number includes minute particles weighing a tiny fraction of a gram and smaller than the head of a pin to those weighing hundreds of pounds. Although little of this stardust reaches the earth's surface as meteors, on its fall through the earth's atmosphere it is converted into microscopic dust that leaves its imprint in the sediments on the ocean floor. The *Albatross* scientists estimated that, if the same amount of meteoric material falls over the whole earth, 10,000 tons fall from the heavens each day.

The calendar read October 1948. The end of the ship's lease was almost at hand. Captain Krafft set out for home as fast as he could go. Just one day before the expiration of the lease, the beautiful white ship steamed into Göteborg amid an ovation even greater than she had enjoyed on leaving. The men on the ship had been very lucky. Every member of the staff had returned well and strong. The only absentees were the few sailors who had been lured to remain in the exotic South Sea islands.

To try to piece together and to interpret the old, old records he had so patiently pried from the time clock of the sea, Hans Pettersson returned to Göteborg and his ancestral home on the windswept shores of the Skagerak.

To the great credit of Professor Kullenberg, when the core samples were analyzed in Göteborg, except for a semiliquid condition in the upper layers, they were in the exact condition that they were in when taken from the deep and as they had lain below the waters of the ocean for untold millions of years.

To make sure the vast amount of material gathered from the depths of three oceans was studied carefully, the cores were sent to specialists in a dozen countries. The specialists have been mainly concerned with the microchemical composition of the cores; their content of radium and uranium, pollen grains, cosmic balls, volcanic ash, red clay, and globigerina ooze; and general biological conditions—all factors that bring to light the incredibly long history of the earth.

The Swedish Deep Sea Expedition brought to light far more information about the age of the sediments than had ever been learned before, but since the study was so new it was difficult to state results with any certainty. Yet the information the scientists are laboriously learning from the cores is a striking example of the relationship of astronomy, geology, physics, and deep sea biology, and of the researches that will be made in the near future.

And certainly in the light of today's oceanic research, the *Albatross* made an especially important contribution to our understanding of the deep seas, for the emphasis at the present time is strongly directed to the investigations of deep sea geology and geophysics.

Undoubtedly every ship that ever set out had a more ambitious program than it was possible to fulfill. The goal of the *Challenger* had been to learn "everything about the sea." Together the *Challenger*, the *Fram*, the *Michael Sars*, the *Albatross*, and hundreds of other expeditions have not been able to do this. Still, equipped with the most modern devices of the day and manned with a group of dedicated men, each expedition has advanced man's knowledge of the seas many fold.

And if you have followed the development of oceanography as a science, even the few attempts to fit together the jigsaw puzzle of the sea recounted in this book, you must be impressed with the increasing complexity of the investigations. With each expedition bigger pieces of the puzzle are slowly being dropped into place and more fundamental problems are being attacked.

When Professor Pettersson speaks of two billion years, or three hundred million years, or even three million, we have the feeling that our local problems are not very important after all, and that in the longtime plans of the "First Great Thought" the threat of atomic explosions, political and economic upheavals, and all the other concerns of our age are only passing irritations. To the thoughtful man of today, it is a comfort to take a long view of the universe and the earth's history.

✿   ✿   ✿

But still man was not satisfied. He wanted to see with his own eyes what lay beneath that indefinite curtain which divides the air and the water.

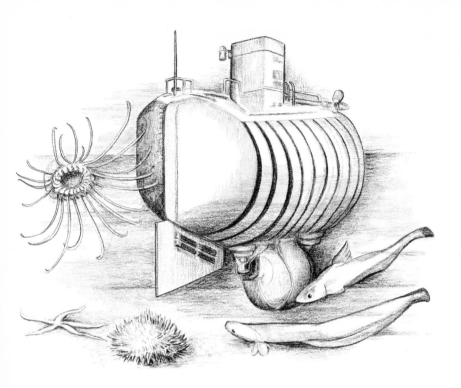

9

Beebe, Cousteau, and the Piccards —
Man Observes the Depths

Full many a gem of purest ray serene
The dark unfathomed caves of ocean bear.

Man was not satisfied with studying the sea with mechanical
devices—dredges, trawls, echo sounders, sediment corers, and
centrifuges. They were too impersonal in their reports. He wanted
to see for himself, to get first hand contact with the world that lay
hidden beneath the illusive curtain at the junction of the air and
water.

But how could he do this? Man's physiology is not adapted to being under water. He is a creature dependent upon the air. However, he believed that there must be some way to enter this forbidden realm. Had not Alexander the Great devised a glass barrel in which he had rocked on the waves for 96 days?

Fantastic tales tell us that Alexander, decked out in his crown and regal robes, sat on a throne chair in a barrel made of glass covered with asses' skins. Under the protection of an angel and supplied with food for many months, he watched the animals in the deep seas, including a monster so big that it took three days and three nights to swim past the royal observer. At the end of the ninety-six days Alexander said, "The marvelous things of God are exceedingly wonderful."

Remembering Alexander's ingenious device and the host of inventors who had contributed to the bewildering maze of gadgets designed for underseas diving, two adventurous Americans, William Beebe and Otis Barton, in the 1920's decided to find a better way of seeing the wonders on the bottom of the sea than by using steel helmets and weighted shoes, the then usual gear. They would construct a cylinder strong enough to sink deep into the water and to return again. Unlike Alexander, whose safety was assured by an angel, they would depend upon steel and quartz, oxygen and rubber to protect them. So Otis Barton set to work building such a cylinder.

By 1929 he had designed and built a steel ball which Beebe named a "bathysphere" for descending into the sea. The sphere, not as tall as a man, was four feet nine inches in diameter with steel walls one and a fourth inches thick and weighed 5,400 pounds. It had three windows made of fused quartz, the strongest material known capable of transmitting light waves of all lengths.

The windows were eight inches in diameter and three inches thick fitting into steel projections. Through one window it was planned to direct a searchlight into the water. Through the others occupants of the steel ball could peer into the underwater world. Each window would hold back the pressure of tons of water. Opposite the windows was an entrance politely called a door, a 400-pound lid that could be lifted on and off with a block and tackle and bolted around a 14-inch manhole, just wide enough for a thin man to squeeze through. The bathysphere would be supported and serviced by a ship at the surface.

To serve as a mother ship, Beebe and Barton procured the *Ready*, a large open-decked barge manned by twenty persons. The *Ready* would lower the sphere into the water on a 3,500-foot nontwisting steel cable seven-eighths inch in diameter with a hauling strain of 28 tons. The barge was equipped with cables, derricks, steam boilers, electric power, winches, and a telephone. The all-important air supply for the bathysphere would be provided by two oxygen trays as well as trays of powdered calcium chloride to absorb the moisture and soda of lime to absorb the carbon dioxide from the air. The telephone was of tremendous importance for through it the operator would keep in touch at all times with the men far below in their sphere. Two winches were provided, one for lifting the bathysphere off the deck and swinging it free of the barge; the other for supporting it while making dives. When not in use, the bathysphere would rest on the deck of the *Ready*.

William Beebe was not a novice in experimenting in new fields. All his life he had been looking forward to the next great adventure. For years as Director of the Department of Tropical Research of the New York Zoological Society, he had traveled to the far reaches of the earth studying natural science—the jungles of Africa, the wildernesses of South America, the deserts of Asia. He had ridden on ships, in submarines, and in airplanes, reaching a height of four miles above the earth. Now he was determined to be the first scientist to actually go into the deep ocean. This he felt would be his most unusual and unearthly adventure.

By the summer of 1930 the bathysphere was ready for its first test. As this strange craft was towed to the lee side of Non-Such Island off Bermuda, where for two years Beebe had been studying the life of the deep sea, the inventors were beside themselves with excitement. All their hopes were pinned on the success of this dive. Along with the men on the *Ready*, they watched the wind and the barometer and prayed for fair weather and absence of squalls. The first descent of the bathysphere was made without passengers, and when it surfaced, seemingly without mishap, great was the rejoicing. All seemed to be well. A number of dry runs being successful, on June 19 Beebe and Barton inched themselves into the sphere, unwound their long legs, and were bolted in. The ship dangled in midair on its cobweb cable for a minute; then it was swung from the deck and lowered into the water at the rate of fifty feet per minute.

In describing the descent, Beebe said that, as the last visible link with the upper world slipped away, he had a sense of complete isolation, as though he were in a plane lost in outermost space. At the depth of 900 feet, he realized that he and Barton were the first living men to look upon the sea at this depth.

As the bathysphere went lower and lower, the light gradually faded. "In turn the red, orange, green and blue rays disappeared leaving only the faintest tinge of violet. Then there was only a blackish-blueness until at 1000 feet every trace of light was gone. Below this depth the world was blacker than black."

So as not to miss the endless array of starfish, sea pens, sea fans, anemones clinging to the cliffs, and fish swimming in front of the quartz windows, Beebe turned on the electric searchlight and pressed his face against the window while Barton checked the temperature, adjusted the oxygen tank, looked for leaks, and kept track of the depth. Beyond 1,000 feet, the intermittent use of the searchlight and the light given off by the animals themselves in a series of luminescent dots or balls of fire were the only sources of light.

Seated on the deck of the *Ready* hundreds of feet above, a secretary equipped with earphones and mouthpiece took notes on everything Beebe said over the telephone. There were so many new sights to see and report that he could not possibly relay them all. He was at a loss to know where to begin. The secretary's notes showed that on that first dive Beebe was particularly impressed by the changing colors, every color in the spectrum disappearing one after the other as the bathysphere descended. Beebe said that in the underwater world all senses except sight were discarded and, like the bathysphere itself, he became simply two huge eyes looking out on a world that for countless centuries had not changed one iota.

At a depth of a quarter of a mile or 1,320 feet, the pressure on every square inch of the bathysphere was 3,366 tons from all directions, but it was so strongly built that it easily withstood the pressure. After an hour of submergence, Barton signaled to the *Ready* to raise the bathysphere. Soon the two men stepped out of the sphere with "the memory of living scenes in a world as strange as that of Mars." A tremendous wave of emotion gripped Beebe as he realized that man through the use of his brain and his inventive genius had been able to conquer the great pressures, the immense depths, and the vastness of the waters.

During a series of dives in the first weeks of August 1932, the bathysphere was plagued by winds, storms, leaks around the quartz windows, and every other conceivable deterrent to success, but finally, on September 22, Beebe wiggled through the door of the bathysphere, made his descent to 1,700 feet, and peered out of the window. Here there was not a hint of light left, all was black. In reaching this depth he had achieved one of the most important objectives of his diving, to get below the level of visual light. "From here down, for two billion years there had been no day, no night, no summer, no winter, no passing of time until we came to record it," he reported.

At 2,200 feet, the lowest level attained in that series of dives, came a fascinating sight. Without warning the water was literally alive with blue parrot fish, hundreds and hundreds of them streaming along as far as the eye could see. These fish, varying in size from six inches to four feet, appeared to be fascinated by the great steel monster that was invading their privacy.

Following the 1932 dives, the strange bathysphere was exhibited in the Hall of Science at the Century of Progress at Chicago, attracting more than half a million people. After the fair closed, the National Geographic Society offered to sponsor a new dive. So in 1934 the bathysphere was completely overhauled, modernized, and equipped for descending half a mile, twice as deep as the earlier dives, into the ocean off Bermuda. On August 11 of that year Beebe climbed over the deck of the *Ready*, bolted the door of the bathysphere, sealed himself in the tiny sphere, and peered out of the window. At once he began to telephone what he saw to the world above. At 25 feet a few aurelia jellyfish drifted by; at 50 feet a school of small thimble jellyfish blurred the window. A flying fish, tufts of sargassum, and great streamers of seaweed floated out from the ceiling of water. Then the red and yellow rays of the spectrum faded out. At 200 feet it was impossible to tell whether the water was blue or green. Copepods and other plankton forms dropped like snowflakes through the upper layers of water on their way to the bottom. At 320 feet pilot fish and a colony of colonial jellyfish, delicate as lace, swam past the windows; at 400 to 500 feet silvery squid and lantern fish added their presence to the scene.

Beebe says that, completely ignoring the artificial light, jellyfish, larval eels, hatchet fish, black angler fish, and pteropods (pteropod ooze is common about Bermuda) drifted by aglow with their own lights. Six fish, genus and species unknown, with big cheek lamps and their bodies covered with a multitude of tiny lights moved through the electric beam. At 2,000 feet there were never fewer than ten pale yellow or blue lights flashing at the same time making a network of animal lights that illuminated an area of two or three feet.

Down went the bathysphere 3,000 feet into the eternal darkness, although everywhere the sea was aglow with living fire. A pair of coppery-sided scimitar-mouth fish swam past; four skeleton fish appeared; a fish as flat as a sole flapped awkwardly along. A large fish carrying a light as big as a ten cent piece on its head swam toward the sphere; then without warning it seemed to explode, bursting into a hundred brilliant points.

Great red shrimps extruded liquid fire and fish whose illuminated teeth had ugly black spaces between them grinned impishly at the intruders. A 20-foot animal, probably a whale or blackfish, without fins or eyes, swept by. Across the screen came fish with green glowing sides and long chin tentacles, while fish with five distinct lines of yellow light each surrounded by purple lamps running the length of the body flashed into view. Then there were slender, silvery eels accompanied by their transparent young. The scene was as brilliant and as colorful as a fireworks display.

Unlike the luminescent plankton in surface water, where the noctiluca and other small animals produce masses of lights, at a depth of half a mile the lights were often individual things, under direct control of the owner. Sparks and flashes and steadily glowing lamps that varied in color, size and position lighted up the darkness. Creatures with no light organs and forever invisible in the deep sea night blundered along. These animals, dependent for guidance upon the glow of other organisms, moved cautiously in and out among the more agile forms. Others, blind from birth to death, whose sole guides are sense organs in the skin and long rays on their tails, groped about as carefully as a blind man taps along with his cane.

The bewildering number of new sights completely intoxicated Beebe. He realized the totally false impression that nets and dredges had given of the myriads of animals in the ocean. With them only the most inadequate sampling could be made, while from the bathysphere he saw animals, large and small, from almost every phylum in the animal kingdom roaming through the waters half a mile down.

When he first ranged through the depths, Beebe says he was quick to see every new sight and was alert in sending his impressions of this world of darkness back to the secretary on the tender boat above, but, as the separation from the upper world became more complete and new sights piled up, his vocabulary used up all its adjectives and his reports by telephone became dull and lifeless. But he never missed the colors. Again and again Beebe tells of the color changes, the colors of the spectrum disappearing one after the other as the bathysphere descended. His mind became drugged and his nerves tense and strained. After two hours in the bathysphere he asked to be raised to the deck of the *Ready*. As he returned to the world of men he reports that he was like a sleepwalker, in a state halfway between fancy and reality.

When after several hours he was able to throw off the dream, he reviewed his notes with the secretary and added details that came to mind. Then with the artist he made crude drawings of the creatures he had seen; later he corrected her professional work by checking size, proportions, lights, color—indeed, all the facts he had noticed through the window of the bathysphere. Since many of these creatures had never before been seen by man, they were, of course, nameless.

Dr. Beebe said that the three outstanding moments of his dives were the first flash of animal light, the eternal darkness, and the discovery of new species of animals. He sums it all up with the statement, "The only other place comparable to these marvelous nether regions must surely be naked space itself, far out beyond the atmosphere between the stars."

For thousands of years man had looked at the sea and had tried in primitive ways to invade it. William Beebe had now succeeded in breaking the surface of the third dimension. He had gone down more than half a mile into the deep dark waters, yet he realized this was only a beginning. He knew that eventually, unhampered by cables and metal spheres, man himself would go deep into the water.

This was Beebe's last series of deep sea dives; thereafter he made short dives to study marine life at scientifically interesting depths. But until his death at 84 in June 1962, at the New York Tropical Research Station in Trinidad, he was still adventuring as a naturalist. During his long life he led more than sixty expeditions to places high above the earth and far below the surface of the sea. Between expeditions he wrote more than a score of books which conveyed a powerful sense of adventure and which were widely read.

*   *   *

The man who soon after the close of World War II was to become famous by going into the sea unhampered by cables and metal spheres was Jacques Yves Cousteau, a captain in the French Navy. He was a man cast in much the same mold as Beebe. Both were tall and thin, restless, creative, and possessed of great social charm. Captain Cousteau had been much impressed by Beebe's modern version of Alexander's glass barrel, but it was not free of earthly restraints. He wanted to tear away all surface bonds.

For years Cousteau had dived in a conventional manner, encased in steel helmet, weighted shoes, rubber suit, and fed air through a tube connected with a tank at the surface of the sea. Wearing this awkward gear he had been able to dive sixty-five feet. Cousteau was determined to find a more satisfactory way of plumbing the deep.

To find this technique, for almost ten years Cousteau and other French naval officers experimented with building a free diving apparatus. While their homeland was occupied by the Germans during World War II, under the guise of secret work, they experimented with this new radical device. As Otis Barton had done, the Frenchmen worked on the principle of buoyancy that Archimedes, the Greek mathematician, had formulated. This states that a body submerged wholly or partially in a liquid is buoyed up by a force equal to the weight of the liquid displaced.

Proceeding on this principle Cousteau and Emile Gagnan, an engineer, constructed a diving apparatus consisting of three cylinders of compressed air linked to a regulator the size of an alarm clock. From the regulator there extended two tubes joining in a mouth piece. With this equipment carried on the back, a pair of goggles or a glass mask on the face, flippers on the feet, and lead weights in the belt, Cousteau and Gagnan hoped to dive unencumbered deep into the sea. The flippers would propel the diver through the water at two knots and his hands would serve as rudders. And so it came about that three Frenchmen—Jacques Yves Cousteau, Frederic Dumas, and Philippe Tailliez—formed a team that introduced aqualunging to the world.

Soon after the aqualung was perfected, Cousteau, with his two companions and his wife, Simone, looking on, prepared for his first big dive. Dumas, acclaimed the best diver in France, would stay on shore ready to come to Jacques' aid if necessary. Simone would keep her eye on her husband by swimming with a snorkel breathing tube. If she saw anything had gone wrong, she would alert Dumas, who would dive to Cousteau in seconds.

At depths of 50 feet Cousteau experimented with loops, somersaults, and barrel rolls. His next adventure was to swim into a cave that to his amazement was crowded with lobsters. He plucked a couple of lobsters from the roof, carried them to the surface, found Simone, and handed them to her. Then he returned to the cave. Five times he did this. Lunching on the delicacies of the cave later in the day, Cousteau, Dumas, and Tailliez built ambitious plans for the aqualung, their new key to the hidden world.

The aqualung allowed the wearer to move about easily in the water at a depth of 100 to 150 feet for an hour or more. With the perfection of the aqualung, its builders realized a whole new way of life had been opened to underwater diving. At last a man could swim like a fish, chase bass, fight with an octopus, or go after stingrays. The diver himself, because of the buoyancy of the water, would feel no sensation of weight. He could stand upside down on one finger or glide propelled only by his flippered feet.

During the summer of 1943 the now famous French diving team made five hundred separate dives. Cousteau reached 130 feet and Dumas swam down to 250 feet. They found that it was possible to descend 300 feet, but the best level is less than 210 feet. To go lower exposes the diver not only to greater pressures than the tank can take care of easily, but to a condition known as the "rapture of the depths" which gives one the sensation of being drunk. (This was a condition not previously encountered.)

Although this deep sea rapture makes one feel carefree and happy, Cousteau says he "fears it like doom." With some divers this intoxication begins at 120 feet; with others at 190 feet. Between 200 and 300 feet aqualungers often pass out. Neurotic persons and intellectuals seem to get "drunk" more easily and suffer acute attacks more often than do "tough" individuals. According to Cousteau the deep sea rapture has only one advantage over alcohol. There is no hangover.

Physiologists believe that the rapture of the deep is brought about by a gradual amnesia caused by too much nitrogen being taken into the body tissues or by too much carbon dioxide being retained in the viscosity of nerve tissues. Because the diver does not realize what is happening to him, the effect is extremely insidious.

In the autumn of 1947 the team made a series of deep dives to study further the effects of the rapture. Maurice Fargues, one of the test divers, at 300 feet signaled, "Tout va bien"—all is well. Then there was no further signal. Rapture of the depths had stolen the air tube from his mouth and drowned him.

Another danger of diving too deeply, staying down too long, or ascending too rapidly is the possibility of suffering an attack of the well-known "bends," which can be crippling or even fatal. The bends is a painful condition often experienced by sponge fishermen and commercial divers caused when a man in pressure breathes too much nitrogen. Instead of passing off in the diver's exhalation, it goes into solution in the blood and gristle. In spite of the dangers of this new sport, aqualunging seized the imagination of the public, and soon men and women and children in all parts of the world "were confidently romping among the jellyfish and the shrimps."

Captain Cousteau explained that in aqualunging, the human lungs have a new role to play, that of a delicate ballasting system. On a dive of 30 feet the pressure is twice that of the surface and with every 33 feet the diver descends the pressure increases 14.7 pounds to the square inch. But a diver feels no increase in pressure because the aqualung feeds him compressed air to meet the new pressure layer. Through the fragile human lung linings the counter pressure is transmitted to the blood stream and instantly spreads throughout the incompressible body. On coming to the surface, the only discomfort the diver feels may be a pain in the middle ear and sinus cavities—a sensation much as one feels when landing in an airplane.

Almost as soon as the war was over, Cousteau persuaded the Marine Ministry of the value of an aqualung diver in doing oceanographic work and in studying sunken and wrecked ships, particularly in making photographs according to the new techniques of underwater photography. The Ministry having agreed to this proposal, the diving team secured the use of the *Elie Monnier*. It was hoped that with a ship at their disposal they could turn their attention to oceanography, for scientists recognized the value of aqualunging in making direct observations of life in the sea. Soon liaison was established with oceanographic and diving groups in Britain, Germany, Sweden, and Italy. During the war the Royal Navy had made a number of studies of the resistance of divers to underwater explosions that they wished to investigate further.

Because Dumas was especially curious about the odd effects of deep water upon the human body, he immediately accepted the assignment by exposing himself to explosions of grenades, shrapnel, and TNT, and an explosive whose name Cousteau could not reveal. After subjecting himself to great dangers from these explosive materials, Dumas concluded that a naked man (an aqualunger) has better resistance to explosives than has a helmeted diver because the helmet often becomes his weakness. It protects his head, but shock waves are intensified by the metal collar and helmet.

The divers next put the lungs to work conducting underwater conditioning classes. Then they took on the job of clearing the waters of Southern France of mines. They were so successful in clearing the mines that in five weeks they located fourteen mines, put charges under them, and cleared the whole area. It was in doing this work that Cousteau and his group successfully developed submarine photographs as a survey tool. This he perfected to a high degree in later work.

Probably the Underseas Diving Group, as the team was now called, got the greatest pleasure from their investigation of sunken ships in the Mediterranean. For centuries Greek sponge divers had dreamed of finding gold and treasure chests in sunken ships, and they had told gruesome tales of encountering fierce monsters guarding the approaches to the ships. The eyes of the sponge diver were not trained to appreciate the beauty of coral growths, encrusting animals, or matted seaweed on the fallen spars of the ships, so they had woven fantastic stories about the wrecks.

Through the help of sponge divers in locating the wrecks, Cousteau and his companions made five hundred dives into twenty-five or more sunken ships, some ancient, some recent, by peering into every hole accessible to a man with three metal bottles on his back.

Cousteau says that the divers never found chests of gold nor were they attacked by octopuses, barracudas, or other so-called sea monsters, but they discovered treasures finer than gold—the art and artifacts of the ancient world—treasures as important as the "digs" of Pompeii or King Tut's tomb.

No doubt the most interesting vessel that the divers came upon was a Greek cargo ship of about 240 B.C. This ship had been located forty or more years earlier, but it had never been systematically investigated. No cargo ship of antiquity is preserved on land and little is known of Greek and Roman merchant ships, so diving from the *Elie Monnier* the Underseas Diving Group was rewarded by extracting from the wreck a number of articles invaluable in filling in some of the blank pages in the history of commercial navigation.

For example, they raised a hundred or more graceful Greek two-handled jars (amphorae) used for wine, oil, water, and grain. Some of these were tumbled and broken, covered with thick layers of seaweeds, corals and sponges. In some unbroken casks the corks were still in place and the sealing wax, bearing the initials of a long forgotten Greek wine merchant, intact. The bottoms of the jars were pointed. On land the points were undoubtedly punched into the ground; when the amphorae were carried on shipboard they fitted into holes in the cargo rack. From the same ship fragments of much fine Delian china were removed.

The *Galley of Mahdia,* a ship first sighted off the Tunisian coast in 1907 by sponge divers, was a "drowned museum" believed to have been built by Sulla, a Roman dictator, who had sacked Athens in 86 B.C. for the purpose of looting her art treasures. Early in the twentieth century, when the wreck was discovered, the sponge fishermen had reported that the bottom of the ship was covered with cannons lying in rows. The director of antiquities in Tunisia aroused art patrons to finance a salvage effort. When the workmen removed the thickly encrusted plant and animal growths from these "cannons," they found them to be Greek ionic columns. But early in the century working in great depths was a dangerous and difficult task, so in 1913 after five years of salvage work the divers gave up the operation.

The French diving team made a six-day survey of this "drowned museum," which was buried in 127 feet of water, but they had neither the time nor the money to study it in detail. It would have cost millions of dollars to raise it. Nevertheless they were successful in finding marble statuary, bronze figures, tall garden vases scattered across the floor, as well as broken jugs, bowls, cups, and saucers projecting from the edges of the muddy mass.

Captain Cousteau concluded that through the centuries, under the weight of the corroding ship, the decks had collapsed and the cargo had fallen into the sea. Perhaps the depth to which the ship had sunk and the limestone walls of a nearby island had prevented the wreck from being scattered by the swell and surf. Today the ship still awaits other divers and other times. What stories that wreck will some day tell of shipbuilding and commerce of the distant past! As a result of Captain Cousteau's study of sunken ships, he is credited with being the first underwater archeologist by scratching for a few days at history's door.

His work in photographing sunken ships led to his unusual and beautiful underseas photography. Using photoflash hand and television cameras, the diving scientists pulled aside the curtain that since the dawn of time had cut man's view from the deep ocean. Now underseas photographers wearing three-cylinder aqualungs took pictures to their hearts' content.

Assumption Island in the Indian Ocean offered an ideal studio for Cousteau and his men to do color photography. Everything was there—comparatively shallow water, a jungle of pink, blue, and purple coral sculptured like stunted trees, umbrellas, crooked fingers, rounded domes, and mushrooms. Small fish—red, yellow, blue, and black—flashed by, while larger species darted among the smaller ones. Reef fish hugged the sea bottom and from the cliffs brilliant sea anemones waved their poisonous tentacles and sea fans swayed back and forth with the currents. Everywhere were animals as rich and varied in color as the hues in a Picasso painting.

Captain Cousteau said, "It was an eerie studio in which we operated. Down from the brilliant surface we would glide, past the cliff dwellings of a thousand fish into the dusk 150 to 175 feet below. Grottoes opened out from the sea wall, dim and inviting. The utter silence of the depths lay upon us like a benediction." Many of the pictures reproduced in Cousteau's book *The Silent World*, a best seller in twenty-two countries, were filmed in this area in water about 144 feet deep.

Captain Cousteau admits he does not know what purpose, if any, the colors serve. Whatever their purpose, he says that there they were, as the camera shows. For taking these pictures four men were required—the model (perhaps a sea fan), the cameraman, and two assistants holding flashlights.

From the deck of the *Calypso,* their laboratory ship, pictures were taken at depths far greater than the men could dive. Captain Cousteau explains in his book that deep down in Davy Jones Locker, with pressures up to 17,000 pounds per square inch, they dangled a 100-pound camera on a braided nylon thread no thicker than one's little finger. With a chunk of pig iron fastened to it, the camera was lowered on a winch to depths of two or three miles. When the line slackened, the photographers assumed the camera had reached the bottom. There for as long as three hours they bounced the camera up and down, hoping that some of the thousands of exposures would occur at the right height and moment to catch a hoped-for snapshot.

In all, the French photographers took 30,000 pictures in the Mediterranean Sea, Red Sea, and the Atlantic and Pacific oceans.

The most tricky and difficult kind of photography that they attempted was to catch on film the much discussed but little understood "Deep Scattering Layer." Roger Revelle, Director of the Scripps Institution of Oceanography, explains this layer by saying that life in the sea is literally living in a goldfish bowl. There is no place to hide and the struggle for survival is so intense that every animal is waiting to devour another creature smaller and weaker than himself. Naturally the predator can spot his prey more easily during the day than by night, so many small animals seek protection by descending to the deep dark water by day, while some instinct impels them to move in great masses toward the upper waters by night where there are rich pastures of diatoms, phytoplankton, and zooplankton. Although he tried a number of times, Cousteau was unable to photograph this moving wall of life.

Cousteau felt that the publicity given to the sounds made by deep sea animals was much exaggerated. To him the sea was a silent world with only the mammals—whales, porpoises, and sharks —emitting grunts and gurgles. He believed that animals react to vibrations in the water much more often than they do to sounds.

Determined to use the aqualungs and their well-equipped ships in as many phases of oceanography as possible, the French scientists were quick to study marine life in its own environment. Dredges and nets snatch specimens from the sea bottom promiscuously, but by direct investigation biologists can determine precisely at what level and under what circumstances these creatures live, and what the relation of one animal is to another.

To cooperate with the oceanographers more directly, Cousteau procured a floating laboratory and a diving platform for making on-the-spot studies of life below the surface. At Malta after the war he had secured an American mine sweeper, the *Calypso*. This was converted into a laboratory by the French Navy and by British and French business firms.

On an autumn evening in 1951, the *Calypso* glided out of the harbor of Toulon toward the Red Sea carrying a number of scientists. The ship was equipped with every modern oceanographic appliance—sonar and radar instruments, fish nets and dredges, automatic pilot, automatic course recorder, a generator for underwater lights, an air conditioned photography laboratory, a collapsible decompression chamber, a ten-ton electric winch, and a small gasoline winch.

On the island of Abu Lott, where the work was to take place, lay an immense field of jagged coral surrounded by a coral lagoon. Eight members of the party armed with cameras swam a hundred feet or more into the water where they saw marine gardens more beautiful than anything they had dreamed of. Everywhere were splashes of color "like the random pattern of an artist's palette." The scientists gathered, harpooned, pried off the rocks, and scooped up so much material for future study that the rafts almost sank under the weight of the collection.

After working with the aqualung for more than ten years, Cousteau began to suspect that it could not be developed much further in investigating the seas. It had shown what man had always suspected. Human physiology will perhaps forever limit his free descent into water much deeper than 300 feet. (The deepest recorded free dive is almost 800 feet.) Cousteau realized that if man is to personally probe the deep waters, he must be encased in some sort of capsule, a new kind of glass barrel. He did not know what this capsule would be, but it would come, he felt sure.

Jacques Yves Cousteau had been a gunnery officer in the French Navy for twenty-two years; he was founder of the Group for Underseas Research; he was the father of underseas archeology and photography; he had received the Legion of Honor Award for his work in the French Underground during the war, and was the author of *The Silent World*. But he was not yet ready to rest on his laurels.

In the early 1950's Cousteau helped the French perfect a bathyscaph, the F.N.R.S. 3; later in the decade he experimented with a baby submarine, a versatile, easily maneuverable diving saucer which he hopes can be used between the depths at which an aqualunger can dive with safety and the rich marine region of the Continental shelf from 600 to 1,000 feet below the surface. Indefatigable Jacques Cousteau is now insisting the sea is such a pleasant place to dwell that he is prophesying that ere long man, living in prefabricated houses will be born, live, and die under the waves. This new man will be called *Homo Aquaticus*.

❖   ❖   ❖

The man who was to devise a "glass barrel" that would go unfettered to the bottom of the world was Auguste Piccard, a tall Swiss physicist with high forehead and disheveled hair. For years he had been experimenting with a ship free of surface fetters that would go to the bottom of the ocean and come back to the surface safely. Piccard's motto had always been, "If you wish to go somewhere and learn something, build a device to do it." When in 1931 he wished to study cosmic rays, those high velocity particles from outer space, he built a balloon that took him up 55,000 feet.

In 1937 this highly imaginative man decided to forsake outer space and to delve into inner space, the depths of the ocean. To do this he must build a depth boat—a bathyscaph. As his predecessors had done, he worked on the ancient Archimedian principle of buoyancy. But what kind of a device could he build that would both sink and float? The answer was to use sea water and iron shot for ballast, while gasoline (which is lighter than water) would provide buoyancy. Working on this principle, Auguste Piccard and his son Jacques wrestled with the problems involved in the operation of a "depth boat."

When in 1948 the bathyscaph was finished, it was really a balloon, but instead of rising into the air, it would rise and sink in the ocean. The passenger cabin was a steel sphere hanging beneath a large float. Such a chunk of steel would naturally sink, so to counteract the weight of the steel the float was filled with 28,000 gallons of gasoline. Access holes permitted water to flow in and out of the float keeping the gasoline at sea pressure.

But the bathyscaph must go down as well as stay up. To compensate for the buoyancy of the gasoline and to initiate the dive, the air tanks were flooded with water, and several tons of iron pellets were added as ballast held securely by electromagnets. When the bathyscaph was to be raised, the required amount of ballast would be dropped; when it was to be made heavier, some of the gasoline would be jettisoned.

The sphere or cabin was reached through a long tube at the end of which was a 300-pound door that looked like the entrance to a small bank vault. The sphere itself was six and a half feet in diameter, just large enough for two persons, the instruments, the controls, and the cameras to be squeezed into. Through two pressure-resistant windows the occupants of the sphere would watch the passing parade.

On November 3 near Dakar the strange blimplike craft was lifted off the *Scaldis*, a Belgian cargo vessel, by a winch and slowly swung overboard, unsupported and untethered.

Auguste Piccard and Theodore Monad, sealed in the metal sphere, made a dive of 14 fathoms which went off without a hitch. The bathyscaph was then to make a dive of 700 fathoms with a robot pilot as the only passenger. The sea was very rough. Everyone was worried. Would she ever return or return too soon to record findings? Finally, after a number of delays, the line was cut and the ship began to settle into the water.

The seamen made wagers on whether she would bob back or remain forever in the graveyard of the ocean floor. The Piccards knew their scientific future rested upon the events of the next half hour. But precisely on schedule, twenty-nine minutes after she had disappeared, someone shouted, "There she is!" Slowly she rose.

When she appeared above the water, her head was bowed in shame. The precious bathyscaph was a sorry looking specimen. Water had leaked into the cabin; the radar antennae were missing; the sphere had been dented by pressure; and the tube for siphoning the gasoline into the cargo ship would not make connections. But what mattered these details? She had done her job. The bathyscaph had descended 4,500 feet and had returned. Auguste Piccard's dream had come true. To be sure some changes in construction and equipment were needed, but the bathyscaph had proved to a doubting world that the principle upon which she was built was sound. She could go to the basement of the world and live to tell the story.

At first it was planned that the bathyscaph would be rebuilt with the cooperation of the French Navy and the Belgium National Fund for Scientific Research. However, delays and disappointments in negotiating for the remodeling, determining the command, and the financing of the ship dragged on endlessly.

After a year or more of disagreements and misunderstandings, the Piccards disassociated themselves from the French Navy. With donations from the people of Switzerland and the enthusiastic cooperation of the people of Trieste, the Piccard father and son set to work to build a bathyscaph that, in honor of the city that had welcomed them so heartily, was to be called the *Trieste*.

On a beautiful day in August 1953 at Castellammare, the *Trieste* was launched. This time there was no robot pilot. The two tall Piccards squirmed into the sphere. With nine tons of iron shot for ballast and 25,000 gallons of gasoline for buoyancy, she settled down into the water in perfect balance. At 22 fathoms Auguste Piccard landed in a beautiful marine garden of anemones and starfish, while glistening red and green algae billowed out from the cliffs.

On their next dive they touched bottom at 595 fathoms or 3,570 feet, landing in soft ooze. The ooze spattered so much mud on the porthole that the view beyond the windows was entirely blotted out. Jacques Piccard poured out iron pellets. With this loss of weight, the bathyscaph began to rise three and three tenths feet per second. As the *Trieste* was lifted toward the world above, the blackness of the deep sea gradually gave way to a gray, then to blue, and finally to the sun-flooded world.

Later in the year the *Trieste* was towed to Ponza, the deepest part of the Tyrrhenian Sea. The bathyscaph having passed all the tests with flying colors, Professor Piccard was sure she was ready to take men to the bottom of the ocean. With utmost confidence in his brain child, Auguste Piccard felt his job was finished and he was getting old. So he retired to his laboratory in Lausanne to ponder further problems of the deep sea. His son Jacques now became the pilot of the *Trieste*. However, for lack of funds few dives were made in 1954.

In the fall of 1955 the future of the *Trieste* began to brighten.

Jacques Piccard flew to London to lecture and appear on television programs. There he met Robert Dietz, an American oceanographer attached to the Office of Naval Research's European office in London. With this meeting the right door was opened. For some time the Piccards had tried to interest the U.S. Navy in the bathyscaph, but without success.

However, Dietz and other American oceanographers were beginning to realize that in this space and missile age the sea, once a protective barrier to a country, was now a dangerous frontier. To study many phases of the sea never before considered, the Office of Naval Research had been set up after the war. Jacques Piccard invited Dietz to visit the *Trieste* in Castellammare. To be sure, the bathyscaph could not fight or run fast, but as a marine scientist Dietz saw its value as a research ship.

Later a number of American scientists visited the *Trieste*. They were particularly impressed by the experiments in sound transmission that could be made on the ship. In his book *Seven Miles Down* Jacques Piccard explains that in deep water sound transmission channels, brought about by salinity and pressure, form a sort of speaking tube along which sound waves travel (five times as fast as in air) over distances as far apart as Hawaii and California. For example, through this sound channel a distant submarine volcanic eruption can be heard across an ocean. Also this underwater telephone transmits noises of fish, porpoises, and snapping turtles.

The *Trieste* put on a good show for the American visitors. Through the plexiglass windows they saw fish, isopods, worms, and crustaceans enjoying their watery world. In many places the sea bottom was perforated with animals holes; flat fish nosed along the bottom, locating their prey with their senses of smell and touch.

As a result of this inspection Jacques Piccard was invited to go to Washington where he and Dietz would plead the cause of the bathyscaph. In the United States Piccard spent 100 days in 1956, "a hundred days that shook my world," he said.

Following this visit, things began to happen—slowly but surely. The *Trieste* would stay in Italy for the summer for a series of at least fifteen dives with American oceanographers evaluating this strange deep sea device.

Eventually in 1958 the United States Office of Naval Research bought the *Trieste*. According to the contract Piccard was to stay with the bathyscaph as consultant and to help in the ship's transition

to a naval group in San Diego, where she would undergo a number
of trial dives in preparation for the supreme test, the Challenger
Deep.

During the trial dives the oceanographers sought answers to a
number of questions, but Jacques Piccard said that it seemed to
him that all they found were more and more questions, so complex
is the ocean.

Early in January 1960 the last trial run was made. The *Trieste*
with Piccard and Dietz aboard dropped 24,000 feet into the Nero
Deep, descending three feet per second (the speed of an average
elevator). They found this a little too fast for distinguishing marine
life easily; things flashed by so rapidly that all the men could be
sure of seeing were a few bits of luminescence. To reduce the speed
some ballast was dropped. Otherwise all the apparatus was in
perfect working order.

Jacques Piccard was impatient to make the "big dive." To him
all dives made so far had been but stepping stones to the one that
would carry him to the Challenger Deep, 36,000 feet under the
surface of the water, a depth no man had attained. It must be done,
argued Piccard. "Until man has placed himself on the bottom of the
deepest depression on earth he would not be satisfied. There is a
driving force in man which will not be stopped if there is yet one
step beyond."

The great day was set for January 23, 1960. Who would make
the dive? Every qualified man in the group hoped to be chosen.
As the fateful day approached it looked as if Jacques Piccard would
not be selected. Impossible! The bathyscaph was the culmination
of his father's life work and he himself had watched over her as
fiercely as a tigress watches over her cubs. But finally, by invoking
a clause in his contract, he was chosen to make the dive along with
Lieutenant Don Walsh, who would represent the U. S. Navy. At
8:15 in the morning of the appointed day the Italian engineer dis-
connected the tow rope from the *Trieste*. The two men entered
the sphere and the steel door was closed and bolted. The fateful
hour had come.

Through the after-porthole Jacques Piccard watched water flowing into the antechamber. The pressure gauge quivered. The ship
was on her way down. All seemed well. Then, without warning,
she bounced upward several yards. She had reached the thermocline, the layer where the density of deep water resists penetration

of the ship. Piccard valved off some gasoline to send her down again. By nine o'clock the ship had descended a mere 800 feet. Beyond the porthole was darkness but not as yet complete darkness. Total blackness came at 2,400 feet. Piccard turned the searchlight into the water. Everywhere tiny bits that looked like snowflakes were falling through the water, but he knew that they were the carcasses of planktonic plants and animals on their way to their final resting place on the bottom of the ocean.

Piccard's plan was for the *Trieste* to fall three feet per second for the first 26,000 feet, then reduce the speed to two feet, and finally, when the ship was 600 feet from the bottom, to one foot. This would break the speed on landing and give the men a chance to see the passing scene more clearly.

Of course, there were a few anxious moments during the dive. A little water trickled into the sphere from the bilge and a couple of mysterious explosions occurred. (The plexiglass window cracked.) At 29,000 feet—as deep under the surface of the earth as Mount Everest is above it—Piccard dropped six tons of ballast to slow the speed of descent to 120 feet per minute or two feet per second.

Here there was no sea snow, not the slightest trace of plankton, only vast emptiness. Piccard remembered Herbert Spencer's words, "I feel like an infinitesimal atom floating in illimitable space." The divers' only fear now was collision with the narrow trench walls which were only a mile apart, and concern whether the bottom would be firm enough for the bathyscaph to land on. Or might it sink and disappear in thick "soup"? At 32,000 feet there were a few traces of life in the water, small jellyfish perhaps. The descent was slowed to one foot per second. The world was very quiet. The echo sounder recorded that there were still forty-two fathoms of water between the ship and the bottom of the ocean. The deepest spot had been pinpointed by TNT charges, the echo delay time being fourteen seconds. Now the descent was very slow. The tension of the two men was at a high point. Illuminated by the electric lights, at three fathoms the bottom was clearly visible, a waste of firm brown diatom ooze. After hovering several feet above the ooze, the *Trieste*, anchored by a few pounds of guide rope, came to rest on the bottom. The *Trieste* was completely unconscious of the 200,000 pounds of water pressing on every square inch of her surface. The depth gauge read 6,300 fathoms—37,800 feet—or 7.2 miles. The *Trieste* had reached the bottom of the world, "the supremest supreme." The time was 1:06 P.M., five hours after leaving the surface. "There it is, Jacques. We made it!" shouted Walsh.

Lying quietly on the ooze was a beautiful red shrimp and a flat solelike fish a foot long and six inches wide, its two great eyes staring at the sphere. Piccard could think of no reason why a fish at this depth should have eyes. The deepest hole in the deepest ocean in the world had been seen by human beings, and the age-old question of whether life existed at the depths of the ocean had definitely and finally been answered. The two men shook hands. They had won. Lunch consisted of twenty chocolate bars.

Suddenly a voice drifted down to them, a voice from the faraway world many thousands of feet above. A telephone had established voice communication without wires or radio waves between the surface and the depths of the ocean. A miraculous first.

Having been recalled to a world of reality by the telephone, Piccard dutifully took the scientific observations. The temperature of the water was 38° F., considerably warmer than at 12,000 feet. The bottom currents were very slow, though life at the bottom was proof of some movement of the waters. No animal tracks could be seen, only a few irregularities in the ooze which might have been made by living creatures. Walsh took tests to determine whether radiation from radioactive sources was measurable. They showed nothing.

Jacques Piccard had waited so long to go to the bottom of the ocean—and he felt so sure that he would never make such a dive again—that he couldn't bear to tear himself away from this weird yet enchanting world. After years of dreaming was he really there? Had he forgotten to make some important observation? For twenty minutes the Trieste lay on the sea floor. Then Jacques Piccard cut off the electromagnet and released 800 pounds of ballast.

The Trieste rose slowly off the ooze, stirring up great clouds of silt. As the ship ascended, the gasoline in the tank expanded, forcing out the salt water. Relieved of her load the Trieste rose faster and faster, breaking the surface in three and one-half hours. By five o'clock in the afternoon the seven-mile elevator ride had ended. The rocking of the sphere told the divers that they had returned to the "heaving breast of the sea." She was back in the world of sunshine and men. And Auguste Piccard had lived to see the fulfillment of his dream. He died in the spring of 1962.

A few days later the historic dive to the bottom of the world was officially recognized in Washington when President Eisenhower presented awards to Jacques Piccard and Don Walsh.

And what of the future? No one could say. Until Beebe, Cousteau, and Piccard had themselves descended into the timeless zone of eternal night, man had had to rely upon dredges, echo sounders, and core samples for information. Now he had seen the bottom of the world with his own eyes. Piccard and Walsh knew that a new era in the study of the sea had been opened up.

❀   ❀   ❀

Shortly before the *Trieste* had gone to the bottom of the sea, the *Nautilus* and the *Skate*, nuclear submarines, had gone under the ice at the top of the world, 90° North.

10

Anderson and Calvert — The Nautilus and the Skate

If I take the wings of the morning and dwell in the uttermost part of the sea, even there will Thy hand lead me, and Thy right hand shall hold me.

The year 1958 was a momentous one in the history of the United States Navy. It was also momentous in the lives of two young Navy Commanders—William R. Anderson and James F. Calvert. During that year the *Nautilus*, the world's first nuclear submarine, made a transpolar voyage from the Pacific to the Altantic Ocean by passing under the ice at the North Pole. As if that were not enough fame for one year, the *Skate*, the third nuclear submarine built by the United States Navy, made a successful crossing under the polar ice in August of the same year, and in March 1959 it stood on top of the world by crashing through the thick blanket of ice that covers the whole Arctic region.

Of course, men had tried to reach the North Pole for centuries, but the cold, the ice, the winds had always defeated them. Finally, in 1910 Robert E. Peary, a Commander in the United States Navy, traveling over the ice by dog sledge, succeeded in planting the Stars and Stripes on that bleak lonely spot. Then came the airplane allowing man to fly over the Pole almost at will. But in 1931 Sir Hubert Wilkins sparked interest in another type of polar travel by proposing to take a submarine to the Pole.

His plan was to duck between the ice floes in the *Nautilus*, coming to the surface in open waters to recharge the submarine batteries. Only after meeting insurmountable obstacles did Wilkins admit defeat. Today Wilkins' *Nautilus* is largely forgotten, but it was this ship and her indomitable commander that were the inspiration of her descendants, the nuclear-powered submarines.

Although Sir Hubert Wilkins' attempt to reach the Pole was a failure, his objectives were almost identical with those of the atomic submarines *Nautilus* and *Skate*. Both the conventional and nuclear submarines hoped to take soundings, obtain water samples at all depths, observe Arctic currents, measure air and water temperatures, attempt radio communication with the outside world, study the formation of the ice pack, measure light penetration, and study the psychological effect of Arctic operations upon the crew of the submarine.

Following Sir Hubert's gallant failure, interest in Arctic submarine travel waned until World War II when, to avoid Allied submarines, Nazi submarines hid under the edge of the ice pack. After the war Dr. Waldo Lyon, a young physicist in the electronic laboratory in San Diego, became curious as to what might happen when a submarine entered a frozen sea. As one step toward this study, he invented a fathometer (ordinarily used to measure the depth of the water), which allowed echoes to bounce upward toward the ice, thus allowing a submarine to measure the depth to which ice fingers hung below the ice blanket.

The next year Dr. Lyon traveled six miles under the ice in a conventional submarine. In 1949 Commander Robert D. McWethy and Dr. Lyon persuaded the Navy Bureau of Personnel to station them on the icebreaker *Burton Island*, which operated by crashing through the ice from one open space to another. Using the icebreaker and Dr. Lyon's gear, they penetrated the ice, then traveled twenty miles, staying submerged for eight hours.

This experiment started a number of men thinking about the possibility of using the new atomic reactor, which did not require recharging for under ice travel. In 1950 Senator Henry Jackson of Washington suggested that it might be possible for a nuclear-powered submarine to travel under the ice. Commenting on Senator Jackson's idea, Admiral Arleigh Burke said, "An interesting suggestion. Let's really look into it." Such a craft might also have military potentialities.

When the decision to build nuclear submarines was finally made, the construction was pushed ahead rapidly, first the *Nautilus,* then the *Seawolf,* then the *Skate.* The *Nautilus* got under way in 1955 with Captain Eugene Wilkinson in command. By 1957 the *Nautilus* was a much traveled ship, having covered 130,000 miles. She had called at dozens of ports in the United States, Europe, and the Caribbean areas and became the toast of the world. (The ship had got her name from *20,000 Leagues under the Sea,* Jules Verne's fictional ship *Nautilus,* as had Sir Hubert Wilkins' submarine.) Having shown her prowess to the world, the new nuclear submarine *Nautilus* was now ready to show what she could do on a challenging assignment.

Many young submarine commanders were eager to be assigned to these new wonder ships. Among these were Commanders William R. Anderson and James F. Calvert, who had worked with submarines since their graduation from Annapolis during World War II. Both had finished in the middle rank of his class. Both lived in Mystic, Connecticut, with their wives and children. Both were in their middle thirties.

Both were ordered to Washington, D.C., within six months of one another for service with Admiral Hyman G. Rickover. Interviews with Admiral Rickover, the father of the atomic submarine, were "famous or perhaps infamous" according to Anderson. The Admiral asked strange tricky questions to test the young candidates —their modesty, their resourcefulness, their imagination. The object, no doubt, was really to separate the more conservative young men from the more imaginative.

During Anderson's hour-long interview, the Admiral wormed his whole life history, almost his every thought, from him. The final question had been, "What books have you read in the last two years?" Anderson said that he fumbled and stuttered. He could not think of the title or author of a single book, although he had read at least two dozen books during sea operations at the close of the Korean War. His mind was a blank. "Goodbye," said the Admiral. Anderson felt he had failed miserably.

That evening Anderson sat down at his desk at home and recalled the details of all twenty-four books. Just so the Admiral would not "think every submarine officer was a stupe" Anderson wrote him a letter giving titles and authors of all the books. With great hesitation he dropped the letter into the mailbox. However, the interview had been far more successful than Anderson had thought, for a few days later an order came for him to report to Rickover's office for duty.

James Calvert, too, faced Admiral Rickover, who interviewed personally every man who hoped to work in his branch of the Navy. The story in the wardroom was that many were called but few were chosen. At the end of the interview Calvert was sure that he was one who had only been called. That night he said to his wife Nancy, "The guy thinks I am nothing but a golfing playboy." The very next day the duty officer handed Calvert a message which read, ". . . Proceed to Washington D.C. and report to the chief of the Naval Reactor Branch, United States Atomic Agency Commission for duty."

When they reported for nuclear submarine training neither Anderson nor Calvert knew much about the bleak frozen Arctic. But under the tutelage of Rickover and Wilkinson they were soon convinced that the Arctic held the most strategic and challenging position of any sea in the world, for it lies directly between the two heartlands in the world. The young submarine candidates soon found that there was a good deal of information on Arctic ice conditions, much of it dating back to Fridtjof Nansen's brilliant expedition of 1893–1896. During World War II a store of information had also been gathered.

So fascinating did the study of the North become that Anderson and Calvert ate, slept, and drank Arctic conditions and relived the experiences of the pioneer explorers who had suffered and died for their dreams. The most fundamental fact about the North was that the region is covered with a blanket of ice averaging ten feet in thickness. There are few land masses in the North. However, the ice is not a solid layer, but is made up of chunks and floes that are constantly moving and grinding against one another. Between the floes are cracks and open lakes. As the ice floes press against one another, they build up hummocks that rise 18 to 25 feet above the ice surface and pressure ridges that jut far below it. At this time no one knew how deep they extended, but possibly a hundred feet.

The training given the prospective nuclear submarine commanders was extremely intensive. Commander Anderson concentrated upon the construction and operation of nuclear reactors, turbines, techniques of ascending and descending through the ice. He gave particular attention to the study of the psychology of men who would be living for long periods under ice.

Commander Calvert's training was in many ways similar to Anderson's. In addition, Admiral Rickover himself spent many hours with Calvert stressing points "concerned with the philosophy of what is important for one's self as well as the organization one works in." The Admiral also emphasized respect for the "value of time and a knowledge of the differences between spending it and killing it." Certainly no man had a greater respect for man's mind than Admiral Rickover.

The more the young officers learned about the nuclear submarine, the more they realized that it was a marvel of engineering and the more eager they became to take this enticing new ship under the ice.

Theoretically, the nuclear submarine is the ideal deep sea vessel. Her ability to descend hundreds of feet allows her to pass beneath the ice, however thick; her nuclear-powered engine requires no air (probably the greatest advantage over conventional submarines). She can stay submerged almost indefinitely. She does not have to risk surfacing. She can go fast or slow as the situation demands. She carries instruments to record conditions in air, ice, or in deep or shallow water. She can control her environment, and the crew suffers no physical discomfort, no matter what surface conditions are like. A nuclear submarine can travel at a sustained speed of 20 knots for long periods on a pound of uranium the size of a grapefruit.

This tiny power capsule is equal to tens of thousands of gallons of conventional submarine diesel oil. On the shakedown cruise the *Nautilus* had cruised 1,381 miles in 89.9 hours entirely submerged. On every count she had shown herself superior to any underwater craft in the world.

In addition to these remarkable accomplishments, Commander Anderson knew that the *Nautilus* afforded perfect comfort and convenience. She is a large submarine, 320 feet long (the length of a football field), 28 feet wide, and measures 50 feet from keel to top of the sail. Since the nuclear submarine power plant requires little space, much more room can be given over to living quarters. The officers' wardroom and the crew's mess are large, bright, and cheerful. (They had been designed and furnished by leading interior decorators.)

The crew's mess, always humming with men playing cards, reading magazines, or studying, can accommodate thirty-six at one sitting. It is equipped with ice cream and coke machines and a coffee urn. (Twenty-eight gallons of coffee are drunk every day.) It has a hi-fi system, a juke box that really plays five numbers for five cents. In a couple of minutes the mess can be converted into a movie theater seating fifty persons who can see the very best films for five cents. There are two showings each day, which gives everyone a chance to see the picture.

On shipboard is a library of six hundred books and a daily newspaper (whose jibes spare no one). On shipboard, too, there is an automatic washer-drier, a complete machine shop, and a photographic dark room. In the tile-decked washrooms each man has his individual steel drawer for his toilet articles; and his own bunk with a foam rubber mattress. The temperature in the ship is perfectly controlled—never varying from 72° F.

In the galley, equipped with stainless steel and white tile, three hundred full meals are prepared each day, in addition to hearty snacks for men going on or coming off watches. (On her maiden voyage the *Skate* carried supplies to serve 18,000 meals without replenishment.)

In short, everything that human ingenuity and the country's resources could provide made for comfort and luxury on the *Nautilus*. She was complete even to a reclining couch.

Much of the comfort was due to the efficiency of the nuclear reactor. Stationed in the center of the submarine, this highly complicated uranium-packed atomic pile (grapefruit-size) provides the energy to drive the submarine through the ocean depths and to make possible all the other electrical devices. The two turbine generators are the heart of the ship, providing abundant electricity for "this city under the sea"—manufacturing not only power for lighting and cooking, heating and air purification, but for the electricity required to control the reactor and to operate the main plant itself. On one side of the reactor are the engineering rooms and on the other the control room and living quarters. At the extreme end of the ship are the torpedo tubes, the only armament it carries.

After nearly a year of study and discipline in Rickover's Naval Reactors' Branch, Commander Anderson was ordered to take over the command of the *Nautilus* from Captain Eugene Wilkinson. To get a general picture of the ice-covered Arctic regions, Commander Anderson (the commanding officer of a naval ship is always called Captain, no matter what his actual rank) and several submarine scientists flew north in a Navy Super-Constellation radar warning plane, skimming scarcely six hundred feet above the ice. Throughout the thousand-mile flight along the underice route the *Nautilus* would take, Commander Anderson sat with his eyes glued upon the awesome scene below.

And so on June 19, 1957, the *Nautilus* headed up the east coast of North America toward the ice cap lying between Greenland and Spitzbergen. Anderson's orders read, "At discretion proceed under the ice in the vicinity of 83° North Latitude and return." "How does one interpret 'vicinity'? Could I go to the North Pole?" Anderson had asked his boss, Captain Thomas Henry. "We have confidence in the *Nautilus* to do the right thing," he replied. "We know you will use the right interpretation." Commander Anderson knew the decision was up to him now. If humanly possible and if the crew fared reasonably well under the ice, he determined to try for that magical spot.

Leisurely the *Nautilus* glided a short distance below the water until she neared Jan Mayan Island where a chunk of ice drifted by, then another and another until before the *Nautilus* stretched a seemingly trackless, unbroken, colorless desert. The ship slipped 300 feet below the cold ice blanket. Yet so comfortable and normal were the living conditions on the ship that while eating dinner in the messroom the men listed to Pat Boone singing "Love Letters in the Sand."

While traveling under the ice, a slight leak developed near the top of the submarine. A crew man turned to the Captain and with a perfectly straight face said, "Too bad, Captain. A hundred million dollar house and the roof leaks."

As the *Nautilus* pushed northward under the ice pack, the Captain often scanned the deep pressure ridges with Dr. Lyon's inverted fathometer looking for a polynya, an overhead lake, in which the ship might surface. Forbidding fingers of ice hung fifty feet below the ice blanket, like dark clouds moving restlessly about. Suddenly on the periscope a streak of light indicating an opening in the ice showed directly above the ship. Anderson ordered the ship to surface. Yet, in spite of extreme care, the periscope struck a chunk of ice, and everything in the periscope went black.

Calmly Anderson decided to use the alternate periscope. But on the next attempt to surface, the second periscope was damaged. The *Nautilus* hurried back to the edge of the ice where she could surface. The crew and officers had been so carefully selected and trained that there was almost no piece of equipment that they could not repair. In a matter of hours the ship was under way again. All went well in the comfortable warm cocoon beneath the ice until she reached 83° North when a fuse in the gyroscope blew out.

Life on a nuclear submarine is completely dependent upon the perfect operation and coordination of every tiny screw and bolt in the mechanism. For a short distance Anderson attempted to navigate by less dependable means but, when the *Nautilus* reached 87°, the longitudinal lines began to run together causing the ship to play "longitudinal roulette," spinning around in a circle. Once more Commander Anderson ordered the ship to make a sweeping turn and head back toward the edge of the ice where the escort vessel, *Trigger*, waited. He hoped that the gyroscope could be repaired as easily as the periscope had been. But this was too difficult to be repaired at sea. There was nothing for the *Nautilus* to do but return home. The ship had not yet reached her goal, but the Captain now knew what to expect in under ice travel and Dr. Lyon had taken enough bottom samples and other oceanographic observations to keep a corps of workers busy for years.

As soon as a new gyroscope was installed, Anderson was ordered to attempt to circumnavigate the globe this time from west to east by traveling through the Bering Sea across the Arctic Ocean to Greenland and Spitzbergen, passing under the Polar ice. While the *Nautilus* was enroute to the West Coast via the Panama Canal, a number of problems plagued the ship—a stubborn leak in the condenser, hard-to-explain fumes, a small fire, a forced surfacing, and a crewman's death.

These problems having been taken care of, the *Nautilus* lay at the pier in Seattle for a few days while Anderson and Lyon made a hurried and top secret flight to Alaska by commercial airline to study the ice in Bering Sea. In Point Barrow, the most northerly town in the United States, the men rode in the city's best limousine, a covered truck; slept in the best hotel, a quonset hut; and ate Eskimo hamburgers costing $1.25. The next morning they made their inspection of the ice and were back in Seattle that same evening.

The following day Anderson took the *Nautilus* out of Puget Sound. Since his orders were for the *Nautilus* to remain unindentified until the trip was completed and an official announcement made, during the first night at sea the Number 571 on her hull was painted over. Clear of the Straits of Juan de Fuca, the *Nautilus* dropped below the surface of the water traveling at twenty knots. The Captain picked up the public address system and said, "All hands, this is the Captain speaking. Our destination this trip is Portland, England, via the North Pole."

The spirits of the crew rose a hundred degrees. They were to be given another chance to reach the Pole. With ever-complete attention to duty, the men stood at their posts. Cruising comfortably along with no motion, the *Nautilus* was as steady and level as is one's own living room floor. The temperature inside the submarine was a pleasant 72°, the relative humidity was fifty per cent. The ship's clocks were set to conform to Greenwich time. The crews worked four hours on, then eight hours off. Everyone agreed the most comfortable way to travel yet devised was deep below the ice.

Three days out of port the *Nautilus* left the warm Japanese current and approached the Aleutian Islands 1,700 miles from Seattle. The depth of the water began to decrease until floating blocks of ice were scarcely a hundred feet above the flat featureless bottom of the sea. In the narrow Bering Strait the *Nautilus* became sandwiched so tightly in the ice that only 43 feet of water lay between the keel of the ship and the ocean floor, while less than 25 feet lay between the hanging curtains of ice and the top of the ship's sail.

The narrow strip of water between Cape Prince of Wales and the Diomede Islands (the large one Russian, the small one American, inhabited by one Eskimo family) is perhaps the most difficult and treacherous body of water in the world to navigate, for it is extremely shallow and dotted with low lying islands. In the winter the ice thickens very rapidly as it is forced against the walls of Bering Strait and the Chukchi Sea, forming a tunnel in which layers of ice jam atop one another pushing the ice ever deeper and farther south.

At one point the *Nautilus* barely squeezed between these gigantic chunks of ice. With the knowledge that chunks sixty feet thick had been known to break loose from the Alaska coast, Anderson once more ordered the conning tower officer to reverse the course, saying, "The door forward is closed."

The only alternative was to circle around St. Lawrence Island where the water was estimated to be deeper, then to cut north off the coast of Alaska. In a number of places here too the water was so shallow that the submarine crawled very slowly lest the top of the sail be damaged by the ice. Again there were only 45 feet of water beneath the keel.

In desperation Anderson looked for a polynya where he could surface, so he could see what the ice conditions were. Finally a small lake opened up and the *Nautilus* inched up into it. Here it dodged and twisted between the ice floes. The sonar machine reported ice ahead off the bow and strange objects in the water. However, one strange object turned out to be a flock of seagulls and another a floating log with projecting roots which made it look like a periscope of a submarine. A huge chunk of ice glittering in the sunshine loomed up like a sailing ship.

But ahead was an endless barrier of ice extending as far as the eye could see. The *Nautilus* dropped to 140 feet. There were only 20 feet to the ocean floor, while above was a huge block of ice which the ship cleared by a miraculous five feet. The men stood at their stations in horror.

Commander Anderson made an agonizing decision. Who knew what might lie ahead? Quite possibly the ice was thicker, the water shallower. As Fridtjof Nansen had done sixty-five years earlier, the Captain decided to turn back. After months of preparation and hope, it was heartbreaking to accept the fact that the *Nautilus'* two attempts to reach the North Pole were failures. But the ice was as unmeasured as the far side of the moon. Anderson did not dare take a chance. In anguish he radioed to Admiral Burke asking for instructions.

The order came back to head for Pearl Harbor. To maintain the secrecy of the voyage every scrap of evidence of the polar attempt (even a pair of slippers bought in Alaska) were locked away as top secret in the safe. When the *Nautilus* surfaced in Honolulu, a 35-foot flower lei was hung on her bow, a band played "Anchors Aweigh," and four beautiful Hawaiian girls danced the hula.

Through the remarkable loyalty and self-discipline of the crew, not a word of the unsuccessful attempt of the ship to reach the Pole leaked out.

At home in Mystic, Connecticut, for a few days before reporting to the Pentagon for further orders, Commander Anderson said that he noticed the tomatoes in the backyard were beginning to ripen and his son Mike's 16-foot runabout needed a new cable. "In these friendly familiar surroundings, the unfamiliar Arctic seemed a million miles away," he wrote in *Nautilus 90° North*.

While in the East Anderson received reports the ice had receded considerably in the past weeks. Now it might be safe to make another try for the Pole. On July 21 the *Nautilus* was again under way from Pearl Harbor and headed north. The blue whitecaps of the tropics gradually gave way to the cold gray breakers of the frigid north, and the submarine once more entered the treacherous waters of the Chukchi Sea. "Where before it had been jammed with ice, it was now free," Anderson joyfully reported.

Dodging blocks of ice, the submarine without mishap reached 70° 45′ North on July 30. As it made its way under water toward Point Barrow, long ice stalactites broken from the pack loomed in the path of the ship, causing her to change her course several times. To the great relief of everyone the water here was deep enough for the ship to clear the deepest hanging pressure ridges. Soon the *Nautilus* was under the true polar pack and comparative safety. A great weight slipped from Anderson's shoulders.

The Captain now felt free to tell the crew that if all went well the *Nautilus* should on August 2 embark upon the most adventurous voyage a ship and her men had ever undertaken—the first underice crossing of the North Pole. The slogan among the men was "North Pole or bust."

Day after day Waldo Lyon collected data on the ice, especially on pressure ridges hanging 100 to 125 feet below the level of the main body, until he had gathered more information about the polar waters than had ever been gathered in the immediate vicinity of the North Pole. At the same time the deep water fathometer was measuring the uncharted ocean floor at 2,100 fathoms. Then the floor rose to 1,500 fathoms, and finally to 500 fathoms. Ringing these deep areas were steep cliffs, rugged mountain ranges, and flat plains.

The ship was almost at her goal. The men on duty clocked the course mile by mile. Those who were off duty huddled near the television set watching the ice passing overhead like moving clouds. Every piece of equipment was performing perfectly. A strange contentment gripped the 116 men aboard. For once there was no joking, no wisecracking. The Captain snapped on the public address system. "All hands. This is the Captain speaking. In a few minutes the *Nautilus* will realize a goal long a dream of mankind—the attainment by ship of the North Geographic Pole. With continued godspeed in less than two days we will record an even more significant first—the completion of a rapid transpolar northwest passage from the Pacific to the Atlantic Ocean."

The Captain glanced at the distance indicator. He began the countdown. "Stand by: 10, 8, 6, 4, 3, 2, 1, Mark, August 3, 1958. Time 23:15. (11.15 P.M. Eastern Daylight Saving Time.) Then for the record he noted the temperature was 32.4° F.; the depth of the water 13,410 feet; the ice detector showed a pressure ridge extending down 25 feet. The crew coined a new word, "fan-damntastic." And fantastic the achievement was.

A hilarious North Pole party was held replete with a North Pole cake and a Santa Claus who berated the men for invading his privacy during his vacation season. While the party was at its height, Commander Anderson wrote a radio message to President Eisenhower and one to Mrs. Eisenhower, who had christened the *Nautilus*. The message to the Chief of Naval Operations simply said, "*Nautilus* 90° North." The messages would be sent as soon as a polynya sufficiently large for the ship to surface was found. "Captain," cracked one of the men, "We should have brought some carrier pigeons with us."

Following previous orders, the *Nautilus* lost no time in reaching the east coast of Greenland. After leaving the ice pack, the ship was to proceed to a secret rendezvous off Iceland where Commander Anderson was to be picked up by helicopter and flown to Reykjavik. There a plane would whisk him to Washington for an interview with President Eisenhower, who would release to the world the news of the accomplishment of the gallant ship.

Commander Anderson rejoined the ship a few days later near Portland, England, where she was given a tremendous welcome. But everyone was eager to get home. In record time the *Nautilus* entered New York harbor where the ship and the men were overwhelmed by the whistles of hundreds of tugs and fireboats and a ticker tape parade. For the moment the *Nautilus* was the most famous ship in the world.

A couple of weeks before the *Nautilus'* triumphal crossing beneath the ice at the Pole, another nuclear submarine, the *Skate*, was ready to set out on her maiden voyage for the North under the command of James F. Calvert. On a quiet moonlit night, the *Skate* slipped her moorings at New London with a ship's company of ninety-seven men and nine civilian scientists. The ship buzzed with speculation as to her destination. No one knew for sure what lay ahead, but everyone sensed he was facing the challenge of his life.

Calvert's orders had said, "When in all respects ready for sea, depart New London and proceed to a point west of Spitzbergen transiting via Denmark Strait and the Norwegian Sea. When satisfied that conditions are correct, proceed under the Arctic pack in the vicinity of the North Pole." That indefinite word "vicinity" again. Exactly what did it mean?

Calvert knew the *Skate's* approach to the Pole was to be a scientific one and that it was to prove the usefulness of the route as a possible commercial and military highway. Nothing definite had been said about the Pole itself.

Naturally the *Skate* was somewhat better prepared for setting out for the North than the *Nautilus* had been on her first attempts to reach the Pole, for she had been able to profit by the early troubles of her older sister. Especially were her compasses more reliable for navigating near the Pole. Navigation is always a difficult problem for a submarine, but navigating under the ice near the Pole was something that even the most skilled pilots knew almost nothing about. All they knew was that within 500 miles of the Pole compasses became unreliable, swinging in all directions.

To prevent the *Skate* from having compass trouble she was equipped with a new invention called "inertial navigation." This was a complicated piece of equipment, but simply stated, a series of gyroscopes "stabilized on a platform deep in the heart of the ship always tends to remain fixed in space, not only in relation to the *Skate* or the earth but also in relation to the entire universe, even to the fixed stars."

Commander Calvert explains that delicate devices in the inertial navigation system sense any motion, whether due to the *Skate* or the earth. "By sensing and remembering the forces that disturb the platform, the system and its computers can determine the position of a ship as she moves about the globe, whether at the equator or under the ice pack at the North Pole."

With confidence that this newly installed navigation system was the answer to the problem of finding their way, the crew was determined to be the first nuclear submarine to get to the Pole. They knew the ship was a good one and they were fiercely loyal to her. They felt strong competition with other submarines, especially the *Nautilus*.

Imagine the men's disappointment and surprise when just before the *Skate* was to drop under the ice near Prince Karl Forland Island, a radio message came in from the British Broadcasting Company: "The world was thrilled yesterday by news that the American nuclear submarine *Nautilus* had crossed from the Pacific to the Atlantic, passing under the North Pole enroute." The rest was drowned out.

Within seconds the news had spread to every corner of the ship. Commander Calvert tried to explain the situation, but the men were in no mood to listen. Calvert sent a message of congratulation to the *Nautilus* from all the officers and crew of the *Skate*.

Routinely the *Skate* dropped three hundred feet below the ice. As the ship passed under the pressure ridges, the ice machine traced a pattern of stalactites hanging from the ice ceiling. The fathometer showed the ocean floor to be 500 feet below. In spite of his disappointment, before each instrument, bank of dials, and machines stood a grim-faced youth faithfully doing his job, but his heart was heavy. Every turn of the propeller was carrying the *Skate* farther into the unknown, into uncharted and endless ice, but now the voyage had no real purpose to the men. Their incentive was gone.

In a nuclear submarine it is possible to cruise for very long periods under the ice. If the ship is to be useful as a military and trade weapon, she must be able to send and receive messages, decipher codes, and to report weather conditions. To do these things, she must be able to surface—and to surface there must be a polynya or open lake between the ice floes through which the ship can rise.

Commander Calvert, who was always deeply conscious of his men's psychological state, wished desperately that he could think of something to distract their minds from the disappointment of being beaten to the Pole by the *Nautilus*. Perhaps surfacing would afford this release. He began to look for a skylight on the ice detector. After scanning the "heavens" for some time, he saw a light spot. He would try to surface. With difficulty he found the exact center of the lake and gave the order to rise.

First the sail, the compartment which houses the periscope—that vital delicate eye of the ship—the sextant, and radio antenna, shoved its head above the water. Then the hull of the submarine herself rose to the surface. From the bridge twenty-five feet above the ice the Captain looked out across an overwhelming vastness of white. The lake on which the *Skate* rested appeared to be only a puddle and the ship puny and weak. In the distance the overcast sky blended into the ice to blur the horizon.

No sooner had the *Skate* surfaced than the off-duty men swarmed onto the ice. Almost instantly in the cool fresh air of the Arctic summer, everyone felt released and free. As if by magic the tension and the disappointment were "gone with the wind" and the usual good-natured banter of men at sea began again. Walt Wittmann, a civilian ice expert, dressed in fur parka and fur boots, and carrying an ice can, a thermometer, and a pair of binoculars hustled onto the bridge. Walt was as devoted to the study of the ice as a painter is to his art, both esthetically and intellectually. Soon others readied the collapsible boat and set off for "shore" to examine the force of the earth's gravitational pull, to test sound transmission, and to find the exact position of the ship by using celestial navigation. This was to serve as a check upon the efficiency of the new "inertial navigation" set. They meshed perfectly.

After an hour's parade across the ice, Commander Calvert's well-trained eye sensed the polynya was beginning to close. The men were summoned back from their sightseeing trip. The rubber boat was deflated, the tanks flooded, the hatches closed, and the *Skate* began to submerge into the calm blue below. Water closed over the submarine's sleek metal sides and she was soon but a speck in the vast ocean.

Walking through the engine room later, the Captain said that he looked "at the pieces of machinery on which we were betting our lives. I stopped by a sleek gray turbine, humming efficiently behind its shining dials and burnished fittings, pouring out electric power that enabled the *Skate* to live. In the harmony of every part it was a thing of beauty." Yet the Captain realized "We who are in charge of this creature of reason must often lean upon a presence beyond reason to find the strength to fulfill our duties in the uttermost parts of the sea."

Calvert now realized that since the *Nautilus* had made a successful crossing of the Pole, there was nothing in the orders to the *Skate* to prevent her from going there too. So, traveling at sixteen knots, she hurried north. Again anticipation and excitement built up in the crew. The nearer the Pole she came the traditional compasses began to act crazily, turning in every direction, yet, controlled by "inertial navigation," the *Skate* kept her course.

Now there was only a mile to go, the ship slowing almost to a crawl. The Captain began the countdown: "4-3-2-1." The *Skate* reached the North Pole on August 11. And on her first try. At least she had beaten the *Nautilus* on that score. "Congratulations to each of you," said the Captain. "But this is only the beginning. Before we are through, we are going to demonstrate that a submarine can come into the ice pack, operate at will, surface when she wants to, and carry out every mission our country requires." "Bravo. We're with you," shouted the men.

The ice near the Pole was so thick, no polynyas could be found through which to surface. As an alternative the *Skate* made a quick trip around the world in a twelve-mile circle in one hour, no doubt the fastest round-the-world cruise ever made. The next order of business was to tell the world of the successful crossing of the Pole, and to visit Alpha Drift Station.

Commander Calvert's orders had read, "If you reach the Pole by the 14th of August, you are authorized to proceed to the vicinity of Drifting Station Alpha." This was one of two stations maintained on the ice jointly by the Air Force and civilian personnel during the Geophysical Year. The stations were simply camps established on the ice for the study of Arctic conditions.

In 1918 Vilhjalmur Steffansson had conceived the idea of such a drifting camp and, though he was not able to participate in it because of illness, his assistant Storker Storkerson and four assistants lived on the ice for six months making scientific observations. In 1937 the Russians established an ice station 34 miles from the Pole on which in one year they drifted 1,100 miles. A later Russian drift party discovered the gigantic underwater Lomonosov mountain chain, one of the most spectacular ranges in the seas.

The *Skate* crew was eager to make a social call to the Drift Station and to see the work being done by this interesting scientific group. (A young oceanographer, Dr. T. Saunders English, who read and criticized the manuscript of this book, was a member of the Alpha Drift party.) Before leaving New London, Commander Calvert had learned the predicted position of Alpha Station for the middle of August. Still no one could forecast its present location with any certainty because the station drifted two or three miles a day.

To communicate the crossing of the Pole to the Navy and to alert Alpha of the ship's visit to her, Calvert searched for an opening in the ice large enough to accommodate the *Skate*. At long last a small lake showed up on the ice indicator. Uncertain of its size, he inched the ship up until she seemed to hover between the walls of a frozen canyon, the ice hanging down in great dark folds like a velvet curtain. With the main body of the submarine resting between the ice curtains, he shoved the hump of the sail up until the instruments inside it could make contact with the outside world.

And thus the news of the *Skate's* transit of the North Pole was flashed to the world via radio Manila. The second message was to Drift Station Alpha, asking their exact location and suggesting they prepare for visitors. When the Station had been established in April 1957, the floe had been about 500 miles from Point Barrow; now in August 1958 it had drifted approximately 900 miles north. At first it was hoped that the floe would move over the Pole, but now it was heading toward Canada. From Alpha came the message, "Best estimate eighty five North, one three six West. Many polynyas in vicinity, but best only fifty yards from our main building." Lieutenant Dave Boyd, officer of the deck, chuckled, "How do you go about finding a place that doesn't know where it is?"

The *Skate* began searching for that one polynya out of a possible hundred in that part of the ocean. As she approached the general area of the Drift Station, the *Skate* was guided by the soft put-put of an outboard motor. (Underwater sound could be heard for six miles.) Gradually the put-put became louder. The ice detector soon indicated open water ahead. The *Skate's* periscope revealed that there dotting the ice were a dozen brown buildings reminiscent of quonset huts standing on stilts. Around the small open stretch of water raced an outboard motor boat, the occupant waving his cap wildly.

In this drifting community located in the "area of inaccessibility," a part of the ice pack extremely difficult to reach, lived twenty-eight men. To moor the *Skate* securely in the polynya, lines were thrown out and the submarine made fast to iron stakes driven into the ice. For the next twenty-four hours the motor boat ran a ferry service from ship to camp where there was much visiting, much gaiety, and much feasting. During a tour of the laboratories a lively comparison of scientific data was carried on, the scientists proudly explaining their coring tubes, heat budget apparatus, water bottles for sampling salinity and temperature of the melt water, echo sounders, radio apparatus, and cameras for photographing the ocean floor and the northern lights.

Commander Calvert even enjoyed the luxury of a telephone call to Admiral Warder in New London, transmitted by an amateur radio operator in Oregon. The only thing that was confusing to the *Skate* crew in this lonely outpost was the time of day. The Station clocks said it was morning while the wardroom clocks said it was evening.

In return for the Station's hospitality, James Calvert invited the scientists to eat dinner on the *Skate*. As an added gesture of good will the Drift cooks offered to trade polar bear steaks for ice cream. (The cooks on the *Skate* threw the steaks overboard as soon as they were out of sight of the Drift station. The odor was more than they could endure.)

However, shortly before the dinner guests were to board the Skate, a large chunk of ice, some thirty feet across, broke loose from the pack and drifted toward the *Skate*. Hospitality ended at that moment. "Recall the crew," the Captain ordered. He had read of polynyas closing so swiftly that ships were caught and crushed between floes like nuts in a cracker. Just before the *Skate* submerged, a bag of letters was thrown aboard stamped with Alpha's own postmark.

Thinking of the scientists who spent a year or more of their lives in this "area of inaccessibility," Jim Calvert commented: "How well these men embodied the meaning of Fridtjof Nansen's remark, 'Man wants to know and when he ceases to do so, he is no longer a man.'"

The *Skate* flew back toward the Pole, surfacing for the fifth time in a week in that now familiar region. Then enroute to Greenland and Spitzbergen she passed under the ice at the Pole for the second time. In Bergen the streets were decked with flags in honor of the *Skate* as they had been when Fridtjof Nansen had set out for the Pole so long ago in his small wooden *Fram*.

On the bottom of the fiord outside Bergen lay the hulk of that earlier *Nautilus*, the dream of Sir Hubert Wilkins. Although he had never met Wilkins, who was now living in the United States, Commander Calvert sent him a message expressing his gratitude for the accuracy of his insight and predictions of nearly thirty years ago. He also invited the now elderly gentleman to be the guest of the *Skate* in New London, an invitation he soon accepted.

Early in September 1958 the *Skate* returned to Boston amid great celebration and rejoicing. In recognition of the submarine's achievements the Navy was already planning an even more difficult task for her. The Pole had been crossed by both the *Nautilus* and *Skate* during the summer, the most favorable season for Arctic travel. If the route were to be of military or commercial value, it must also be navigable in the winter when the whole North is shrouded in darkness, when the ice is extremely thick and extends far to the south.

The all-important question was whether during the winter polynyas could be found, and how a nuclear submarine could break through the winter ice to communicate with the outside world. Commander Calvert was eager to attempt a winter crossing, for in recent conversations with Wilkins and Steffansson, both men had suggested this as the next step. However, if such a crossing were to be attempted, several changes would have to be made in the *Skate*, particularly in strengthening the sail.

According to the new plans the sail would in effect serve as a battering ram to break through the ice. Floodlights and a special closed circuit television set must also be installed.

Workmen were soon swarming from one end of the *Skate* to the other. One day, while the repair work was going on, Admiral Warder called Calvert to the telephone. The Admiral said he had just received a request from friends of Sir Hubert Wilkins suggesting that the *Skate* carry the ashes of this submarine pioneer to the Pole and scatter them there. (Sir Hubert had died several weeks earlier.) "The *Skate* would be honored," Calvert answered.

On March 3, 1959, the *Skate* was ready to sail for the Pole, the second time in seven months, with practically the same crew reassigned to her. It was time too for James Calvert to say "Goodbye" once more to his family. To Calvert and his wife Nancy partings were now almost routine. They knew time passes and returns are sweet. For the children, however, "Goodbye" meant goodbye. Just as his father was leaving the house, three-year-old Charlie toddled to the car and entreated, "You won't be gone so long this time, will you, daddy? Back so-o-on?"

Like a veteran the *Skate* slipped beneath the troubled surface waters of winter and set her course for Prince Karl Forland Island,

4,000 miles away, where she submerged. The ice was much farther south now than it had been in August. Continually the ice detector scanned the ceiling for patches of thin ice, but it showed nothing but black jagged fingers hanging down as far as thirty feet. The only thing that relieved the blackness was an occasional school of small fish dashing along in such numbers that they seemed to push the ship along, while large fish with open mouths and flashing eyes chased them. All the polynyas of last summer were closed and frozen. The prospect of finding a skylight seemed hopeless.

The *Skate* was now less than 250 miles from the Pole traveling at 16 knots in her warm cozy berth. Even in the winter a layer of thin ice must eventually show up, argued the Captain. On that possibility, he cruised back and forth under one area. After crisscrossing it a number of times, a faint glimmer of light showed on the periscope. It looked far too small to hold the ship, for it was surrounded on all sides by black pressure ridges. To attempt to surface was a dangerous and delicate task.

Yet Calvert had to seize the chance. The *Skate* rose to within 100 feet of the surface. At that moment the ice drifted over the skylight and all was black again. Soon more thin ice showed above. In order not to lose it, the tanks were emptied and the ship moved slowly upward. "Ready to surface. Stand by to hit the ice," ordered the Captain.

Suddenly there was a sensation like an elevator being stopped too quickly. A heavy grinding crunch shook the control room. The top of the sail disappeared from the television screen. In ramming the ice, a radio antenna had been bent. To repair the antenna Lieutenant Al Kellin, radio officer, strapped to the mast rode up thirty-five feet to thread in the new part. Working with bare hands in 20° below zero temperature, he soon had the antenna in working condition. All was well for the moment. The whole ship was above the ice, the bridge covered with shattered chunks. A crew man armed with a crowbar tossed the ice blocks off the side of the submarine.

Commander Calvert climbed the ladder, squeezed between the remaining ice, and looked about him. "The pale blue melt ponds of last summer were gone. In their place was a world of whiteness. Setting off the ghostliness of the ice was a beautiful soft sky of rose and lavender where the morning sun peeped over the rim of the frozen world." (It would rise no higher.) The *Skate* had proved that she could ram her way through the heavy ice.

The next goal was to surface at the Pole, which was only a couple of hours away, but to find a skylight was another matter. The *Skate* criss-crossed several times below a tiny gleam of emerald green light. The ice was moving so rapidly that it was hard to stay beneath the opening. Finally, by estimating the speed of the movement, the Captain felt safe in saying, "Stand by to surface at the Pole."

The tanks were blown. The *Skate* moved slowly upward until the upper hatch rammed through the ice, which was so heavy that instead of falling onto the bridge, as it usually did, it split and fell clear of the ship. A fierce wind howled, carrying swirling snow particles as sharp as grains of sand. Heavy clouds over the Pole gave the impression of a stormy twilight. In the 26° below zero temperature the men's breath froze on their chins. All about were hummocks 18 feet high.

The *Skate* had surfaced at the North Pole, the first ship in history to do so. At once preparations were made for the burial services of Sir Hubert Wilkins. Calvert had not said much about the service to the men for fear that it would be impossible to surface. Now feeling a deep sense of reverence, he asked that a small altar made of boxes and covered with a green cloth be set up. The bronze urn containing the ashes was placed on the table. To provide light for the reading of the service, crew men held flares on each side of the altar. A rifle squad formed near the bow of the ship. Above the ship's sail whipped the flags of the three countries Sir Hubert had loved—Australia, Britain, and the United States. The high wind, the intense cold, and the lurid light made it difficult for the Captain to hold the prayer book; nevertheless, solemnly and distinctly he read: "I am the resurrection and the life, saith the Lord: He that believeth in me, though he were dead, yet shall he live; and whosoever liveth and believeth in me shall never die. I know that my Redeemer liveth." Lieutenant Boyd picked up the bronze urn and, followed by the Captain and the two torch bearers, walked 30 feet from the ship. While the Captain read the committal service, Boyd tossed the ashes into the wind, where they disappeared in the half darkness and the swirling snow. The rifles cracked three times in a final salute. Sir Hubert Wilkins had reached his final resting place. In spirit the service was not only for Wilkins but for all the brave men who had spent their lives in the conquest of the North.

Before leaving the Pole the men built a cairn of ice blocks in which they placed a message dated March 17, 1959, stating that the *Skate* had surfaced at the Pole and had conducted a memorial service for Sir Hubert Wilkins. In due time, the Captain said, this message may, like the wreckage from the *Jeannette,* be carried by the drift to some distant shore. (You remember it was the finding of a cap belonging to a crew member of the ill-fated *Jeannette* that convinced Fridtjof Nansen that the Pole could be reached by drifting with the current.)

Once more the *Skate* turned homeward. After several unsuccessful attempts to surface in areas where the ice seemed as hard as concrete, she finally was able to ram her way to the surface in a world of brilliant stars, a three-quarter moon, a gentle breeze, and a 23° below zero temperature, a world of beauty and purity. Several of the men went swimming encased in quarter-inch-thick sponge rubber suits which completely covered them except for their faces.

Unfortunately, while the ship was surfaced, the seal on one of the water pumps broke loose, spraying water everywhere. Dave Boyd reported that it would take 12 hours to make the repairs. In spite of the piercing cold, he set to work repairing the pump. After the ship had been surfaced a couple of hours, the ice mass began to move, slowly at first, then with thundering crashes as ten foot blocks tumbled together like children's building blocks being torn down.

As the ice moved rapidly toward the *Skate,* the rumble of the grinding grew deafening. Somewhere, probably hundreds of miles away, gigantic forces were at work pushing millions of tons of ice inexorably toward the tiny man-made ship. Feeling certain his beloved ship would be crushed into bits between the great ice masses, Commander Calvert decided that the only hope of saving her was to submerge in spite of the unfinished repairs, He was about to give the order when miraculously the grinding stopped almost as suddenly as it had begun.

At six thirty in the morning Boyd knocked on the Captain's door. He looked exhausted, his eyes bloodshot, his face haggard. Calmly he reported, "Repairs completed. Ready to submerge, Sir." The job had been finished in less than seven hours.

The *Skate* sped on toward Prince Karl Forland Island where on March 27 she passed out of the ice after ten surfacings and 3,090 miles of underice travel and headed for New London. In answer to Calvert's report to the Navy that the *Skate* had carried out her two assignments, a radiogram "Well done" came from Admiral Arleigh

Burke. Admiral Rickover later presented to Calvert a bronze paper-
weight on which he had scribbled, "Oh, God, the sea is so great
and my boat is so small."

Calvert's highest praise for the success of the expedition went,
however, to the ship's crew, "The men were the *Skate*," he said.
"Together they had faced the unknown and had made it the familiar. Together they had learned many of its [the sea's] secrets,
its perils, its uses, its austere beauty." He was sure that he ex-
pressed the feelings of all the men in the words with which he
concludes his book, *Surface at the Pole*. "Lord, now letteth thou
thy servant depart in peace, according to thy word. For mine eyes
have seen thy salvation. . . . . ."

❁   ❁   ❁

Having reached the top of the world by surfacing at the Pole,
man now determined to reach the interior of the earth by boring
to the mantle.

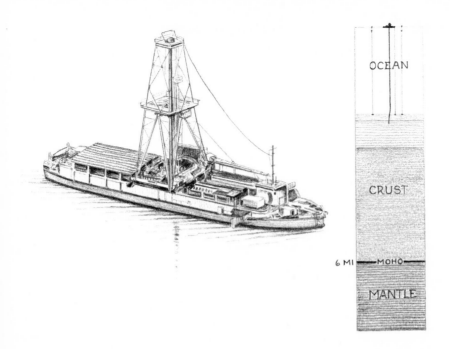

11

Willard Bascom —
The Mohole Project

That which is far off and very deep, who can find it out?

To many scientists the idea of drilling a hole through the bottom of the sea into the mantle of the earth seemed almost as fantastic in 1957 as Jules Verne's story *Twenty Thousand Leagues Under the Sea* had seemed in 1869. Some belittled the idea by likening it to Sir Conan Doyle's fictional professor who dug a hole into the earth in *When the Earth Screamed*. Or even to Edgar Rice Burroughs' character who found the inside of the earth a hollow shell of rock inhabited by great hairy animals.

In fact, critics compared the Mohole Project to any of the ten-foot shelves of books in which authors have "bored and burrowed into the interior of the earth like literary termites," said Willard Bascom Director of the Project. Yet looking backward today the Jules Verne tale might well have been a blueprint for the Mohole Project.

To the small group of scientists from the Scripps Institution of Oceanography in La Jolla, California, however, the project was a very serious undertaking and if it were accomplished one which would reveal undreamed of facts about the history of our planet.

As the stories of the many expeditions discussed in this book have shown, for a hundred years oceanographers have probed into the seas wresting secrets from the almost three-fourths of the earth that is water. Each expedition has made its contribution to man's knowledge by bringing to light some hitherto unknown facet of this "great waste of waters."

But the most far-reaching undertaking of all was planned in 1957 by curious, restless, striving *Homo sapiens*. He now wanted to find out of what the interior of the planet was made. If he were to learn this basic fact of ancient history, he must probe much deeper into the earth than anyone had yet dreamed of doing. For some time earth scientists had suspected that hidden many miles beneath the blue green curtain of water that laps upon our shores is written the life story of the earth—perchance from the very time of its solidifying.

When this bold project was first suggested by a group of imaginative young scientists at the Scripps Institution, few of their fellow scientists took the idea seriously. The undertaking seemed impossible of achievement.

No doubt the possibility of such an undertaking had been fomented in the minds of these men for some time, but the idea was discussed for the first time in April 1957 as the Scripps group gathered for an informal breakfast at the home of Walter Munk in La Jolla, California. As the practical attainment of such a project was argued back and forth, the men became so excited that the discussion continued into the dinner hour and beyond in the home of Roger Revelle, Director of the Scripps Institution. The more the men argued the more reasonable and exciting the idea became. That such a drilling would take place sometime they felt sure. So why not begin to plan it now? On the spot Gordon Lill, founder of the American Miscellaneous Society and head of the Geophysics Branch of the Office of Naval Research, was named chairman.

Certainly from time to time men had suggested that holes be drilled into the earth for some particular purpose. Among the first of these was Charles Darwin, who in 1881 wrote a letter to Alexander Agassiz saying, "I wish some doubly rich millionaire would take it into his head to have borings made in the Pacific and Indian atolls and bring home cores from a depth of 500–600 feet for examination" (to study the growth of coral atolls). Too, many suggestions for deeper oil borings had been made. But the plan for finding out about the inner substances of the earth seemed to many persons, even in this age of scientific discovery, to be going too far.

By combining innumerable bits of indirect evidence gathered over many years a hypothesis of the structure of the earth had been worked out; a solid inner core, a molten outer core, a mantle, and a crust. It was thought that eighty-five per cent of the earth is mantle made of a very hard rock which extends down 1,800 miles, whereas the crust is a thin veneer averaging ten miles in thickness, a mere four hundredth part of the radius of the earth.

Of the structure of the earth below the crust man's ignorance was almost as complete as it was in Jules Verne's day. The tiny fraction of information available to us about the mantle had been derived from measurements made by seismologists studying the paths and velocities of earthquake waves. To the Scripps scientists much more knowledge of the structure of the earth seemed vital if the study of oceanography were to continue to extend our knowledge of the seas.

In 1909 a great boost had been given to the study of the earth's mantle by a distinguished Yugoslav scientist, Andriya Mohorovicic, of the University of Zagreb. While studying earthquake waves on land and sea, he had found that the earth was layered—a thin surface layer of light rock at the top (the crust), separated from heavier materials beneath (the mantle). While watching a seismograph Professor Mohorovicic had noticed a sudden jump in the velocity of earthquake waves from one layer to the other. This jump in velocity he believed marked the boundary between these two entirely different formations. In honor of Professor Mohorovicic this line of demarcation was called the Moho Discontinuity. The project to drill to the Moho was called the *Mohole*.

At the upper edge of the Moho where the mantle meets the crust,

Professor Mohorovicic saw that the velocity of earthquake waves ranged from 15,000 to 20,000 feet per second, while below it they traveled 25,000 feet per second. To the professor this increase in velocity proved conclusively that there was a decided change in the formation of the earth at this point, for it was known that the greater the velocity at which sound waves travel, the denser is the material through which they are passing. The depth and thickness of the various sediments and rock layers on the ocean floor and thus the depth to the bottom of the earth's crust can be made by estimating the seismic records of wave travel time.

This discovery raised all sorts of questions and set in motion a long train of conjecture as to how the earth came to take its present form and the possibility of man's being able to make direct contact with the far-off mantle. To many persons this seemed harder to reach than the moon (and perhaps it is). At least it seemed very remote until that Sunday in 1957 in La Jolla.

From that day the same urgency drove the earth scientists to find out about the rocks beneath the crust of the earth as impels the astronauts to penetrate outer space. John Steinbeck, a long-time amateur oceanographer, who became excited about this experiment, said, "If we can seriously plan and design stations in space and on the moon, we are surely capable of mining a few thousand feet under water. The engineering problems are far simpler." A wag in La Jolla quipped, "Surely the earth's bottom is at least as important to us as is the moon's behind."

The more the Scripps scientists thought of attempting this project, the more excellent reasons they found to support it. Willard Bascom said that the successful operation of the project would settle once and for all the unsolved mystery of what the bulk of the planet is really like. It would help answer the question of the age of the earth; the thickness, structure, and composition of various layers; perhaps even the origin of the ocean and of life, and how the earth came to have its present form. And it would allow man to look deep inside the earth and far backward in time. Without question it would stand out as one of the twentieth century's most significant achievements. It might even pose questions and answers that no one has yet dreamed, for, says Mr. Bascom, unpredicted discoveries are often the most important result of new work. In fact, the enthusiastic young proponents of the idea saw no limit to the information it would open up.

As soon as word of the serious discussion of the Mohole Project got out among scientists, an onslaught of criticism was raised against it.

Yet the idea survived all criticism. The important question was how this small group of scientists at the Scripps Institution could get support for such a far-reaching and unusual project. If it were ever undertaken it would probably require years of planning and many millions of dollars to carry it out. Unfortunately, too, such an undertaking did not fit into any of the traditional branches of scientific research.

To ease the financial problem, the California scientists asked aid from the American Miscellaneous Society, an esoteric group with branches throughout the United States and several foreign countries. This society, called the AMSOC, a mild satire on the alphabetical scientific societies, was founded in 1952 for considering research ideas that didn't belong in any organized group— "crazy offbeat ideas," perhaps. In spite of its earlier reputation, AMSOC had opened up new avenues of thought and research in a number of fields and was now on a solid scientific basis. The Miscellaneous Society had no officers, no constitution, and no formal membership. Mr. Lill, however, appointed a special Mohole Committee under the sponsorship of the powerful National Science Foundation to consider the request of the Mohole group for aid. (With deep regret they turned down the request.)

But the men were not discouraged. The group had already enlisted support for the project at the 1957 meeting at the International Union of Geodesy and Geophysics held in Toronto. After a great deal of discussion and much criticism, the project as outlined by Gordon Lill was approved. It carried unanimously.

The nations of the world, especially England and Russia and others experienced in drilling, realized its possibilities. (The Russians said that they already had the equipment for such a drilling.) With the backing of this powerful group, the Mohole scientists went to work in earnest making plans and surveys for possible drilling sites, yet knowing it would take many years of quiet planning before a final thrust could be made. Soon many of the best known and most respected scientists in the U.S. had been added to the Mohole Committee.

Today, because of the immensity of the undertaking, the amount of planning involved, both engineering and geological, the new techniques to be developed, and the great cost, the Mohole is still in the testing stage. Therefore, this chapter of *Explorers of the Sea* is the story of the preliminary work, thought, and experimentation that go into a great research project in science.

The first step in planning this project was to find out if it were scientifically possible to reach the mantle, and if so where it came closest to the surface. Geologists had already pointed out that the earth's crust beneath the oceans is thin, in many places not more than three to five miles, while beneath the continents, it is much thicker. For example, under the island of Puerto Rico the crust is about twenty miles thick, whereas under the ocean just beyond the island it is only two to four miles thick with 18,000 feet of water above the floor.

Physicists, who study the inaccessible portions of the earth by means of instruments such as the seismograph, explain this difference in the thickness of the earth's crust by their belief that the continents and islands are great sheets of relatively thick light granite, while the ocean basins are floored with thinner, heavier basaltic rock. Both types of crust are apparently floating on the much denser rock of the mantle.

By using the term "floating," geophysicists liken the continents to icebergs which in order to rise a little above the surface of the sea must extend a long way beneath it. In the same way, if a mass of rock—a continent, a mountain range, a large island—stands high, it is compensated for by a heavy foundation.

By 1959 the Mohole scientists had done much research, made many surveys, and carried out a number of geological and geophysical studies. Numerous pin-pricks of possible drilling sites had been made. Early in the study the planners rejected continental shelves, volcanic ridges, ocean deeps, and areas of high heat flow, as well as areas of cold and stormy weather, strong currents, and long distances from bases of supplies. They studied the structure of the sea bottom, made continuous echo soundings, gravity, and seismic measurements, and took numerous piston cores of the all-important sediments. Studies at various locations were made of winds, waves, swell, and surface currents.

They finally selected two possible sites for early experimental drilling—the North Atlantic Basin near Puerto Rico, and the waters off Guadalupe Island, a couple of hundred miles southwest of San

Diego, as sites meeting many of the requirements. To get more exact information on these areas, a reconnaissance survey was made in the Atlantic Deep north of Puerto Rico (already one of the most widely studied regions in the Atlantic Ocean) by four ships sponsored by the National Science Foundation and the Office of Naval Research. For nearly a month these research vessels crossed and recrossed the area making seismic refraction measurements of the thickness of various sediment and rock layers by the echoes of exploded depth charges.

The immediate purpose was to find out whether the Puerto Rico area was geologically representative of the earth's crust. Almost at once the geologists found that to reach the Moho a short distance from Puerto Rico it would be necessary to drop a line through 18,000 feet of water and then to bore through 14,000 feet of sediment and rock. This did not present an impossible undertaking in itself, but the men were not able to measure the ocean currents here. Unless the current is slow, the site will probably not be used for the final drilling, for everyone realized one of the biggest problems would be to hold the 18,000 feet of unsupported drill pipe steady against a strong current.

The men agreed too that the Atlantic Ocean is extremely stormy, "No job for the faint of heart, the light of muscle, the weak of stomach." And the work calls for a love of the ocean, boats, and scientific work not often found even in oceanographers.

The next question was what kind of ship could be used for drilling a hole beneath the bottom of the ocean. The natural answer was to use the techniques that the engineers in the oil industry have developed in the past hundred years. On land oil wells have been sunk 18,000 feet many times, a few to 25,000 feet. One oil expert believes that his company can reach 50,000 feet on land.

On land, however, the depth to the mantle may be 100,000 feet, far beyond the reach of present-day technology. So the scientists decided to move the oil drilling technique out at sea for an experimental Mohole drilling, where, as we have learned, the distance to the mantle was about 32,000 feet. Of course, oil drilling had been done offshore, but only in shallow water and on continental shelves. In 1953 holes had been drilled in the sea bottom from a floating bargelike vessel called the *CUSS*, owned by the Continental, Union, Shell, and Superior Oil Companies (and from whose initials it took its name). The vessel was used to keep the operators of these companies informed of offshore operations and of the direction of oil research.

After testing and examining a number of drilling devices, the AMSOC group concluded a *CUSS* type of ship was well suited as a base of operations for securing basic drilling know-how in water 1,000 to 10,000 feet deep.

Fortunately in 1959 Mohole engineers and scientists had no conception of the innumerable complications involved in drilling a hole in the bottom of the sea. Had they known the difficulties, they might well have concluded it was "a crazy idea."

At any rate the AMSOC group secured for an experimental ship a war surplus navy barge—260 feet long and 48 feet wide—which was redesigned on the principle of the *CUSS* at a cost of $2,700,000.

Already four years of time, toil, faith, and millions of dollars had gone into the project, so with a ship of their own everyone was eager "to go and see what it could do." Even the most optimistic did not expect the *CUSS I* (as the new ship was named) could drill to the Moho. Early in the spring of 1961 it was towed to a station twenty-five miles west of San Diego, California, where five experimental test holes were made in water 3,146 feet deep.

Encouraged by the results of these tests, late in March the *CUSS I* was moved for her dress rehearsal to a site between the Mexican coast and Guadalupe Island at 117° 30′ West Longitude and 29° North Latitude, where she held position for three weeks in 11,730 feet of water.

Previous surveys had shown Guadalupe to be an excellent place for drill operations. The depth made the tests meaningful; the bottom was reasonably flat; the weather was usually favorable; surface currents and winds were moderate; the area had been surveyed by geologists and seismologists; the sediment layers were estimated to be about 700 feet thick; seismic reflection surveys indicated a second sediment layer probably lay below the first one.

Everyone connected with the work realized that neither the ship nor the equipment was strong enough to reach the Moho, but the thrust would show whether the general techniques were feasible and whether by using them this layer that "was far off and very deep" could at some future date be pierced. In simplest terms, the conventional method used in oil drilling would be employed, "a long pipe to rotate a weighted bit which chips and grinds away the material in the hole. The rock chips and cuttings are washed away from the bit and brought to the surface by a thin mud that circulates down inside the drill pipe."

John Steinbeck, who since his University days at Stanford had been interested in oceanography, was invited to accompany the *CUSS I* to Guadalupe to report the story of the rehearsal to the world. "I am aboard," he wrote in *Life* magazine, "because of a long time interest in oceanography and some small experience in matters of the sea. I am privileged and greatly excited."

In his colorful style he described the *CUSS I* as having "the sleek lines of an outhouse standing on a garbage scow" as it waddled toward its position. Then seriously he added, "The importance of the craft's mission belies the oddity of her looks. For her scientists hope to bring back samples of rock never before penetrated, materials rich in information about the earth's beginnings and structure."

The tug that was valiantly pulling the dead weight of *CUSS I* and its thousands of tons of equipment toward Guadalupe on that March day in 1961 seemed very small. The men on the "ship" knew that the island was a high, waterless mountain whose top is fringed with conifers and inhabited only by goats, a herd of sea elephants, and a small Mexican radio crew. While the *CUSS I* inched her way toward Guadalupe, Willard Bascom called everyone together—the cooks, seamen, drillers, and all the others, and gave them a lecture on the history of the project and explained the part geology and geophysics plays in revealing the history of the earth. The men listened attentively to Mr. Bascom and the talk pulled them into a unit. They now knew what the drilling was all about and each felt he had a part in the exciting and epoch-making undertaking of reading the history of the earth through the strata of rocks far below the water.

Mr. Bascom explained that if undisturbed layers of material can be raised from deep in the earth, man should be able to read the age of the rocks just as he now reads the age of a tree by the growth rings in the trunk. He also pointed out that the rock strata would be much more revealing than are the tree rings because the strata have lain undisturbed for millions of years.

About midnight of the second day out from San Diego, according to Steinbeck, the tug reached the drilling station off Guadalupe, which had earlier been positioned by the *Spencer Baird,* a Scripps Institution ship. As soon as the tug neared the drilling station, it dropped the *CUSS I* and four great outboard motors pushed her between buoys that were to serve as anchors.

At once the engineers realized that in dropping a line through thousands of feet of water and then drilling into the rock beneath, the hardest problem would be to hold the ship steady. (The wind was now blowing 30 knots.) For months oil companies, metal makers, equipment manufacturers, and AMSOC scientists had argued about the theoretical and practical problems of doing this.

The rule of the sea is that objects in it do what the water does. Since the water moves continually, the question was how scientists could hold the ship stationary enough to drill a hole into the rock two and three tenths miles below the water. After long debate on techniques for anchoring, the engineers decided to attempt to hold the ship within a permissible drift of three per cent of the depth of the water by using a dynamic-positioning system in which the thrust of constantly rotating propellers would be balanced against the natural forces of winds and currents.

Specifically this would be done by a complicated system of deep-moored buoys installed around the drilling site and operated by a skilled pilot on the ship, who would watch blips and pinges on the radar and sonar screens. These blips are made from echoes received continuously from strategically placed radar buoys on the surface and sonar buoys beneath it. The pattern made by the blips and pinges would tell the pilot at any given moment whether and where the ship was drifting. If the ship were drifting beyond the safe limit, he could compensate by manipulating the motors.

The *CUSS I* was simply a barge with a derrick standing ninety-six feet above the waterline. The designers hoped that it was strong enough to withstand winds of terrific force and to support working loads of 300 tons. Inside the derrick tower was the floor where the drillers worked. At the top of the derrick was the "crown block," a huge block and tackle arrangement that carried the load. Below the crown block hung a traveling block that moved up and down within the derrick. This was equipped with a hook that supported the' mammoth load. Everything going into or coming out of the well was raised or lowered on these blocks.

Through a center shaft drilling pipes and instruments for measuring temperatures, magnetism, and porosity also descended. In addition *CUSS I* was loaded with electronic equipment, much of it designed for this project, as well as with motors, and mud storage tanks. All this equipment was operated by a huge power plant.

John Steinbeck insists though that "the most important and unique equipment of the *CUSS I* was the group of men aboard, an elite and motley crew." Most important perhaps were the drillers, whom he called "roughnecks." Aboard too were hardworking engineers and scientists of many kinds—oceanographers, geophysicists, seismologists, geologists, paleontologists, petrologists. (You may have to use your dictionary to figure out the special work of some of these "ologists.") In appraising the crew he said, "Our expedition should destroy the old and well loved error that thinkers and doers are different breeds, and about time too."

The minute the *CUSS I* was in position, Steinbeck noted that the drilling team was ready to go to work stringing the drill pipes which were to extend all the way from the ship to the sea bottom thousands of feet below. Lying horizontally on the deck to keep the center of gravity low and to avoid the danger of the pipes shifting with the roll of the ship were tons of steel pipes four and a half inches in diameter and 60 feet deep.

As skillfully and as easily as though they were adding beads to a necklace the drillers began to send the drill pipes toward the bottom of the ocean 11,730 feet below. The string dangling beneath the ship was as limber as though it were a rope swaying in the wind. Yet it must support by its own strength about 125 tons of weight. At the business end of the string a mushroom-shaped diamond drill with $8,000 worth of commercial diamonds at the cutting edge would bore its way through hundreds of feet of sediment below the water, and if luck were with the project, into the rock below the sediment.

To lengthen the pipe string continually, an elevator yanked a 60-foot section of pipe from its horizontal position. The pipe swung into a vertical position where it dangled from the pulley block. At the rate of one a minute, the drillers guided a section of pipe until it met the previous length where with a spin their thread ends met. One by one the sections of pipe dropped into the shaft in the center of the ship and disappeared into the depths. At several places where there was particular stress on the drill string, bumper subs and guide shoes—flared funnels which prevented excessive bending of the pipes—were placed.

Steinbeck says that it was wonderful to see those big, powerful, hard-hatted drillers work. They were the cream of a very special profession whose teamwork was marvelous, each one performing his difficult job with perfect precision and timing. And these drillers had enormous pride in their work. All day the pipes dropped toward the sea floor, the men working in 12-hour shifts.

The drill pipes dropped through the water with little resistance, but finally the echo sounder, that remarkable scout that forewarns of coming events far down in the sea, told the men above that the drill bit was approaching the bottom of the sea. It also sent up news that the floor of the sea was a great plain of low rolling hills. The excitement rose to high pitch. A central coring tube two inches in diameter to bring back sediment and rock samples was in readiness. The core is hauled to the surface by a wire line inside the drill pipe.

The big problem from this point on, and upon which the success of the Guadalupe test hinged, was the ability of the pilot to hold the derrick directly over the hole through which the diamond drill was to bore. Should the barge sway more than three per cent of the depth of the water or 360 feet, the pipe might snap. If this happened, the recoil would jar the craft and the crew might be killed or seriously injured. (If the pipe is removed from a drilling hole, there is no way to get it in again.) To avert such a disaster, the pilot did not relax his attention for a minute from the radar blips or the sonar pinges.

As the drillers dropped more pipes, the wind rose to 30 or 40 knots with waves eight to ten feet high. The CUSS I lurched and swayed. Rigmen lashed and chained down everything movable. Scientists protected their precious instruments, while electronics men glanced nervously at their dials and switches.

The CUSS I roared with noise—motors, engines, whining dynamos. Scientists hovered over the echo sounders. Instruments were sent down to measure the unknown deep currents. They were moving less than a knot in a slow circle. It was too exciting for the men to go to bed. This was an historic moment.

After what seemed a very long time the diamond bit hovered just above the sea floor. Then it touched, certainly the most critical moment in the whole operation, for no one had penetrated to this depth before. Slowly, very slowly, the steel pipes began to revolve

20 to 40 times a minute. (About the speed of a long playing phono-graph.)

The diamond drill began biting into the sediment. What would that sediment be like? The scientists could hardly wait to find out. When the drill had penetrated 110 feet below the floor, a geophysi-cist who could endure the emotional strain no longer dropped a cable and brought up the center bit without interrupting the drill-ing. The core barrel appeared, the long silvery tube flashing in the sun. In it were 21 inches of globigerina ooze, sediment made of tiny fossils that had dropped in a slow ceaseless snowstorm from the earth's surface over a period estimated at 20,000,000 years. It was the same gray-green ooze which covers over sixty per cent of the ocean floor.

Very carefully the core was pushed out of the barrel into a plastic case. "This is valuable material," said Willard Bascom. Even the tiniest trace of sediment was scraped off the barrel to be examined later. The crew, with coffee cups in hand, crowded around to see this precious gift from the depths. The concentration was intense, for this was everyone's project. (However, some of the seamen whispered to one another that they didn't see anything in this "stuff" to get so excited about.) Huge floodlights on the swaying drill rig made the barge look like an immense sea-going Christmas tree. The occasion was indeed worthy of an important celebration, Steinbeck said.

With utmost skill, despite the winds and the storm, the pilot kept the barge within a dozen feet of the hole by manipulating the four large outboard motors, two on each side. As the work progressed, he became so expert he could hold the *CUSS I* as unmoving as though it were planted on a concrete platform instead of on a heav-ing, restless sea.

In the next attempt to bring up a core sample, the corer was lost. This was a bitter disappointment. Frustrating as the delay was, the men quickly replaced the corer. Down went the pipe string once more. The diamond drill worked on biting ever deeper into the gray-green ooze. At 230 feet another core sample was raised—still the same ooze.

At 490 feet the sediment was a denser, darker clay with lighter colored veins. Was the drill entering a different substance? The echo sounder sent up word the drill should soon reach rock. And it did. Just under 600 feet the bit was slowed to two miles an hour. (A diamond drill, working in hard rock, will probably wear out in three or four days.)

What was this hard material? Excitement became intense. Drilling was done with great care. The brake man never took his eyes off the revolving shaft. If the revolutions increased, he eased off the power and held a quarter of a million pounds of drill string steady, lest it snap in two. The drill ground its way into the hard rock.

The corer brought up a great chunk of basalt—stark blue and very hard with crystals extending from it. This was indeed a new find. (The scientists guarded this chunk of rock like tigers protecting their young. Steinbeck felt very guilty when he stole a tiny piece of the basalt for a souvenir.) Then the drill broke through into soft ooze again with pieces of basalt and volcanic ash embedded in it. Could this be a second layer of sediment forecast by the echo sounder? The gray clay was mixed with dolomite, a common mineral, but not often found on the sea bottom.

The finding of sediment consolidated into rock in the second layer was very exciting to geologists, for this might crack the great geological mystery of what had happened to all the sediment that was presumed to have fallen to the floor of the ocean. At the average rate of sedimentation (about two inches in a thousand years) and the length of time sedimentation has no doubt been going on, scientists expected that there should be ninety per cent more sediment than had been found.

An on-the-spot superficial inspection of these second layer sediment cores threw some light on the mystery. The top part of the second layer was not hard-packed sediment but basalt, mixed with dolomite and volcanic ash as well as fossils and ancient sediment from the land, which must have come from a lava flow.

The CUSS I probed 44 feet into the second sediment layer. What this layer is really like it was impossible to say with any certainty. But, apparently, sediment has been overlaid with lava several times, something like a chocolate cake—a layer of cake, than a layer of frosting, one above the other.

After penetrating 610 feet into the sediments (Hans Pettersson's longest sediment core in 1948 was 70 feet) the scientists decided that by using techniques never before attempted the CUSS I had brilliantly fulfilled the promise of the test drill. To be sure almost

18,000 feet of sediment and rock still lay above the Moho Discontinuity guarding the secrets of the earth's genesis. Yet judging by the *CUSS I*'s performance the scientists were convinced that the mantle can be reached. The long-dreamed-of Moho, the point at which the earth's crust and mantle meet, will, with a stronger ship and more powerful equipment, yield to man's genius.

For three weeks the *CUSS I* remained on position off Guadalupe, digging five more test holes; then she was towed back to California, her mission to date accomplished. With renewed enthusiasm the scientists returned to their laboratories and the engineers to their drawing boards, to wrestle with even more complex problems than they had solved up to this time.

Mr. Bascom says that, of course, no one can say exactly what direction future plans for the Mohole Project will follow, but many requirements have already been recognized. First, a drilling ship must be so expertly designed and built that it can stay on station for a year or two. The most critical problem of design is still to keep the roll of the ship at a minimum so that the least possible motion is transmitted to the drill pipe.

The ship must carry living facilities for a hundred men; a complete stock of supplies for drilling: pipes, mud, cement, spare parts, a complete repair shop. It must be equipped with maneuvering propellers of 1,200 horsepower, automatic steering equipment, high pressure pumps, riser pipes, buoys, draw works, etc., etc., etc. Then there must be well-equipped laboratories for half a dozen different kinds of scientists. Certainly a formidable assignment for any naval architect.

Neither does anyone know where the final drilling to the Moho will be or of what kind of rock the mantle is made. (Perhaps periodotite, dunite, eclogite. Have you ever heard of them? Our heads begin to swim as we try to learn all the new terms.) Some scientists suggest that the rock at the top of the mantle may be the original material of which the earth was made and that the present crust has been added by volcanoes. Without doubt somewhere deeply hidden under unnumbered tons of sediment, rock, and lava is the original face of the earth. "That which is far off and very deep, who can find it out?"

Recently a group of scientists has decided to try to reach the mantle by probing into St. Paul's Rocks, a few hundred miles from the eastern tip of Brazil. Their assumption is that these barren rocks may have been spewed up from deep within the bowels of the earth and therefore may be composed of the same material as was the original ocean floor. (These rocks are so barren not a particle of vegetation grows on them, not even a lichen.) To tell the truth, scientists are so uncertain what the mantle is like that they are not sure they will recognize it when the drill reaches this long anticipated place.

Mr. Bascom feels that so much time and thought have of necessity been given to the many practical engineering problems of drilling into the Moho that some of the engineers and scientists are apt to forget the real objective is to obtain scientific information about the history, structure, and behavior of the earth. Of course, the practical problems of technique must be solved before a successful drilling to the Moho can be made. When the practical problems of technique have been solved, and the drilling is completed, there will probably be a continuous core sample of rock 2.5 inches in diameter and three miles long.

What a story of times past that core will tell the geologic historians. It may well be the most fabulous history book in the world. Each scientist will analyze the findings from the standpoint of his own interest. Some will be particularly curious about radioactivity, velocity of sound, intensity and direction of the magnetic field, and temperatures far below the seas. Others will be concerned with the motion of oceanic water masses, including a continuous record of the velocity and direction of the ocean currents, the circumstances relating to waves moving along the thermocline—the boundary between the warm layer of surface water and the colder water below. Still others will want to analyze the structure of the rocks and to study the fossils embedded in the strata.

When the Moho is reached, the scientists hope to install instruments in the hole that will continue to collect data for years, particularly "in-hole" seismographs. Possibly so much preliminary investigation has never been required of a single ship or group of scientists.

The Mohole scientists too have charted a staggering program for themselves. Even when the drilling is completed, the work will be only half done, possibly only a quarter done, for the materials and data must be analyzed and interpreted (a pioneering job even more far-reaching than the *Challenger* had undertaken).

Finally, Willard Bascom prophesies, will come the task of fitting the new information into the old. Without question the new data will be more accurate and may give us an entirely new concept of the changes that have taken place in the earth during the 2,000,000,-000 or more years since it solidified, turning all earlier ideas of the earth's construction topsy-turvy.

No one knows when the ambitious Mohole Project will be carried out, possibly not for four or five years, and it will cost millions upon millions of dollars. However, the early criticism and the skepticism of the experiment have long since gone and the world is eagerly awaiting the completion of this daring undertaking.

Even when the Moho has been reached and many new pieces of the marine jigsaw puzzle have been set in place, man will still be going to sea with questions, for virtually our entire planet remains to be explored. He will still be pondering new and more difficult enigmas whose solutions will make greater demands upon his imagination and ingenuity. At the present time the value and significance of future findings can scarcely be imagined.

The Mohole scientists, as did the marine pioneers of earlier days, will have opened the way for others "to go and see."

Suggested Readings

Chapter 1

MAN DISCOVERS THE SEA

(Books of General Interest)

BERRILL, N. J. *The Living Tide.* New York: Dodd Mead, 1951.

BERRILL, N. J., and BERRILL, JACQUELINE. *1001 Questions about the Seashore.* New York: Dodd Mead, 1957.

CARSON, RACHEL. *The Sea Around Us.* New York: Oxford University Press, 1951.

CARSON, RACHEL. *The Edge of the Sea.* Boston: Houghton Mifflin, 1955.

COKER, ROBERT ERVIN. *Great and Wide Sea.* Chapel Hill, N. C.: University of North Carolina Press, 1947.

DARWIN, CHARLES. *The Voyage of the Beagle.* London: Smith, Elder, 1839.

DEACON, G. E. R. *Seas, Maps, and Men.* "An Atlas-History of Man's Exploration of the Oceans." Garden City, N.Y.: Doubleday, 1962.

ENGEL, LEONARD, and EDITORS of *Life. The Sea.* New York: Time Incorporated, 1961.

FREUCHEN, PETER. *Book of the Seven Seas.* New York: Julian Messner, 1957.

FREUCHEN, PETER, and SALONANSEN, FINN. *The Arctic Year.* New York: G. P. Putnam, 1958.

RAITT, HELEN. *Exploring the Deep Pacific.* New York: W. W. Norton, 1956.

ROSE, J. HELLEND. *Man and the Sea.* New York: Houghton Mifflin, 1936.

RUSSELL, F. S., and YONGE, C. M. *The Seas.* London: Frederick Warne, 1928.

YONGE, C. M. *The Seashore.* London: William Collins, 1949.

Chapter 2

MATTHEW FONTAINE MAURY—PATHFINDER OF THE SEA

LATHAM, JEAN LEE. *Trail Blazer of the Sea.* Boston: Houghton Mifflin, 1956.

LEWIS, CHARLES LEE. *Life of Matthew Fontaine Maury, Pathfinder of the Sea.* Annapolis, Md.: The United States Naval Institute, 1927.

MAURY, MATTHEW FONTAINE. *Explanations and Sailing Directions* (4th ed.). Washington, D.C.: C. Alexander, Printer, 1852.

MAURY, MATTHEW FONTAINE. *Physical Geography of the Sea.* New York: Harper, 1855.

MAURY, MATTHEW FONTAINE. *Maury's Wind and Current Charts.* Washington, D.C.: Naval Observatory, 1857.

Chapter 3

CHARLES WYVILLE THOMSON—THE *CHALLENGER*

Challenger Reports. 50 vols. Originals housed in British Museum, London.

HERDMAN, SIR WILLIAM. *Founders of Oceanography and Their Work.* London: Edward Arnold, 1923.

MOSELEY, HENRY. "Notes of a Naturalist." *Challenger Reports.* London: Her Majesty's Stationery Office, 1892. Vol. XXIV, pp. 540 ff.

SVERDRUP, H. U., JOHNSON, MARTIN W., and FLEMING, RICHARD H. *The Oceans. Their Physics, Chemistry, and General Biology.* New York: Prentice-Hall, 1942.

THOMSON, C. WYVILLE. *Depths of the Sea.* London: Macmillan, 1873.

THOMSON, SIR C. WYVILLE. *Voyage of the Challenger. The Atlantic.* New York: Harper, 1878. Vols. I and II.

Chapter 4

ALEXANDER AGASSIZ—THE *BLAKE* AND THE *ALBATROSS*

AGASSIZ, ALEXANDER. *The Three Cruises of the Blake.* Cambridge, Mass.: Museum of Comparative Zoology Bulletin, 1888. Vol. XIV.

AGASSIZ, ALEXANDER. General Report on the Scientific Results of the Expedition to the Eastern Tropical Pacific, by U. S. Fish Commission, steamer *Albatross* from Oct. 1904–March 1905. Cambridge, Mass.: Printed for the Harvard Museum, 1906. Vol. XXXVIII.

AGASSIZ, ALEXANDER. *The Coral Reefs of the Tropical Pacific.* Cambridge, Mass.: Printed for the Harvard Museum, 1904. Vol. XXXVII.

AGASSIZ, R. G. (ed.). *Letters and Recollections of Alexander Agassiz.* Boston and New York: Houghton Mifflin, 1913.

MAYER, ALFRED GOLDSBOROUGH. *Alexander Agassiz.* Washington, D.C.: Annual Report of Board of Regents of the Smithsonian Institution, 1910.

PEARE, CATHERINE OWENS. *A Scientist of Two Worlds.* (*Louis Agassiz*). Philadelphia and New York: J. B. Lippincott, 1958.

Chapter 5

FRIDTJOF NANSEN—THE *FRAM*

CALVERT, COMMANDER JAMES F. *Surface at the Pole.* New York, Toronto, London: McGraw-Hill, 1960.

NANSEN, FRIDTJOF. *Farthest North. The Voyage of the Fram and the Fifteen Months' Sledge Expedition.* Westminster, London: Archibald Constable, 1897. Vols. I and II.

NANSEN, FRIDTJOF. *The Oceanography of the North Polar Basin.* London, New York: Longmans Green, 1902.

NANSEN, FRIDTJOF. *The Norwegian Polar Expedition, 1893–1896. Scientific Results.* Ed. FRIDTJOF NANSEN. Published by Fridtjof Nansen Fund. Christiania, Norway: A. W. Brogger, 1904.

NANSEN, FRIDTJOF. "Protozoa in the Ice Floes of the North Polar Sea," *Norwegian Polar Expedition.* Published by Fridtjof Nansen Fund. London, New York: Longmans, Green, 1906. Vol. V.

SVERDRUP, OTTO. "Escape from the Ice," *Farthest North.* Westminster, London: Archibald Constable, 1897. Vol. II.

Chapter 6

MURRAY AND HJORT—THE *MICHAEL SARS*

HJORT, JOHAN. *Some Results of the International Ocean Research.* Edinburgh: Scottish Oceanography Laboratory, 1908.

HJORT, JOHAN. *The Human Value of Biology.* Cambridge, Mass.: Harvard University Press, 1938.

MURRAY, SIR JOHN. *Report on Deep Sea Deposits based on Specimens Collected during Voyage of M.H.S. Challenger in the Years 1872–1876.* London: Her Majesty's Stationery Office, 1891.

MURRAY, SIR JOHN. *The Ocean, a General Account of the Science of the Sea.* New York: Henry Holt, 1913.

MURRAY, JOHN, and HJORT, JOHAN. *The Depths of the Ocean.* London: Macmillan, 1912.

Chapter 7

ALISTER HARDY—THE *DISCOVERY* (1927–1929)

BAKER, A. DEC. "Distribution and Life History of *Euphausia triacantha,*" Discovery *Reports.* London: Cambridge University Press, 1959. Vol. XXIX, pp. 309–40.

DEACON, G. E. R. "A General Account of the Hydrography of the South Atlantic Ocean," Discovery *Reports.* London: Cambridge University Press, 1933. Vol. VII, pp. 173–238.

GUNTHER, E. R. "The Habits of Fin Whales," Discovery *Reports.* London: Cambridge University Press, 1953. Vol. XXV, pp. 115–35.

HARDY, A. C. "Work of the R.R.S. *Discovery* in the Falkland Island Dependencies," *Geography Journal,* VXXII (1928), 209–34.

HARDY, A. C. "The Continuous Plankton Recorder," Discovery *Reports.* London: Cambridge University Press, 1936. Vol. XI, pp. 459–509.

HARDY, SIR ALISTER C. *The Open Sea. The World of Plankton.* London: Collins, 1956.

HARDY, A. C., and GUNTHER, E. R. "The Plankton of the South Georgia Whaling Grounds and Adjacent Waters, 1926–1927," Discovery *Reports.* London: Cambridge University Press, 1936. Vol. XI, pp. 1–456.

KEMP, STANLEY. "Progress of *Discovery* Investigations." *Nature,* CXXIV, 483–86 (1929).

KEMP, STANLEY, HARDY, A. C., and MACKINTOSH, N. A. "Object, Equipment, Methods," Discovery *Reports.* London: Cambridge University Press, 1929. Vol. I, pp. 143–229.

OMANNEY, F. D. *The Ocean.* London, New York, Toronto: Oxford University Press, 1961.

Chapter 8

HANS PETTERSSON—THE *ALBATROSS*

BERRIT, G. R., and ROTSCHI, H. "Chemical Analyses of Cores from the Equatorial Pacific." Reports of the Swedish Deep Sea Expedition, 1947–1948. Göteborg, Sweden: Elanders Boktryckeri Aktiebolag, 1957. Vol. VI, pp. 51–58.

KOCZY, D. F. "Echo Sounding." Reports of the Swedish Deep Sea Expedition, 1947–1948. Göteborg, Sweden: Elanders Boktryckeri Aktiebolag, 1955. Vol. IV, pp. 99–129.

KULLENBERG, BORJE. "Deep Sea Coring." Reports of the Swedish Deep Sea Expedition, 1947–1948. Göteborg, Sweden: Elanders Boktryckeri Aktiebolag, 1955. Vol. IV, pp. 35–96.

PETTERSSON, HANS. *Westward Ho with the Albatross.* New York: E. P. Dutton Company, 1953.

PETTERSSON, HANS. *The Ocean Floor.* New Haven: Yale University Press, 1954.

PETTERSSON, HANS. "The Voyage." Reports of the Swedish Deep Sea Expedition, 1957. Göteborg, Sweden: Elanders Boktryckeri Aktiebolag, Vol. I.

PETTERSSON, HANS. "Cosmic Spherules and Meteoric Dust." *Scientific American,* Vol. 202 (May, 1960), 123–32.

WEIBULL, WALODDI. "Sound Explorations." Reports of the Swedish Deep Sea Expedition, 1947–1948. Göteborg, Sweden: Elanders Boktryckeri Aktiebolag, 1955. Vol. IV, pp. 1–31.

Chapter 9

BEEBE, COUSTEAU, AND THE PICCARDS— MAN OBSERVES THE DEPTHS

BEEBE, WILLIAM. *Arcturus Adventure.* New York: G. P. Putnam, 1930.

BEEBE, WILLIAM. *Half Mile Down.* New York: Duell Sloan & Pearce, 1934.

COUSTEAU, JACQUES YVES. "Fish Men Explore a New World Underseas," *National Geographic,* CII (October 1952), 431–72.

COUSTEAU, JACQUES YVES. "Under Water Wonders," *Life,* XXIX (March 25, 1960), 119–24.

COUSTEAU, JACQUES YVES. "Diving Saucer Takes to the Deep," *National Geographic,* CXVII (April, 1960), 571–86.

COUSTEAU, CAPTAIN J. Y., with JAMES DUGAN. *The Living Sea.* New York: Harper and Row, 1963.

COUSTEAU, CAPTAIN J. Y., with FREDERIC DUMAS. *The Silent World.* New York: Harper, 1953.

PICCARD, JACQUES, with THOMAS J. ABERCROMBIE. "Man's Deepest Dive," *National Geographic,* CXVIII (August, 1960), 224–39.

PICCARD, JACQUES, with ROBERT DIETZ. *Seven Miles Down.* New York: G. P. Putnam, 1961.

Chapter 10

ANDERSON AND CALVERT—THE *NAUTILUS* AND THE *SKATE*

ANDERSON, WILLIAM R., Commander U. S. Navy. "The Arctic as a Sea Route of the Future," *National Geographic,* XCV (January, 1959), 21–24.

ANDERSON, WILLIAM R., Commander U. S. Navy, with CLAY BLAIR. *Nautilus 90° North.* Cleveland, New York: World, 1957.

CALVERT, JAMES F., Commander U. S. Navy. "Up Through the Ice at the North Pole," *National Geographic,* XCVI (July, 1959), 1–41.

CALVERT, JAMES F., Commander U. S. Navy. *Surface at the Pole.* New York, Toronto, London: McGraw-Hill, 1960.

Chapter 11

WILLARD BASCOM—THE MOHOLE PROJECT

ARMAGNAC, A. P. "Hole to Probe Mysteries Inside the Earth," *Popular Science,* CLXXV (November, 1959), 85–89.

BASCOM, WILLARD. *A Hole in the Bottom of the Sea.* Garden City, N.Y.: Doubleday, 1961.

BASCOM, WILLARD. "Mohole," *Scientific American, CC* (April, 1959), 41–49.

LILL, G. G., and MAXWELL, ARTHUR E. "The Earth's Mantle," *Science, CXXIX* (May 29, 1959), 1407–410.

MATTHEWS, S. W. "Scientists Drill at Sea to Pierce Earth's Crust," *National Geographic, CXX* (November, 1961), 687–97.

STEINBECK, JOHN. "High Drama of Bold Thrust Through Ocean Floor. Prelude to Mohole," *Life, L* (April 14, 1961), 110–18.

STIMSON, THOMAS E., JR. "Drilling a Hole Through the Bottom of the Sea," *Popular Mechanics, CXVI* (July, 1961), 86–89.

"Test Drill Holes," *Science News Letter, LXXX* (April 15, 1961), 226.

Index

Adaptation to environment, 98–99
Admiralty, 33, 37
Agassiz, Alexander, 54–73, 201
  achievements, 64–65, 72–73
  Albatross expedition, 65–67, 71
  Blake expedition, 60–64
  Croyden expedition, 69
  disposition of wealth, 73
  early life, 55–56
  friendship with Thomson, 58–59, 62–64
  Harvard Museum of Natural History, 62, 73
  Marine Animals of Massachusetts Bay, 57
  scientific papers housed in Harvard Museum, 67
  Seashore Studies in Natural History, 57
  source of wealth, 58, 64
  theory of coral reefs, 57–70
Agassiz, Louis and Elizabeth, 54–57, 59, 73
Agassiz, Maxmillan, 65, 73
Airplanes, use of, 132–33
Albatross Expedition
  Agassiz, 65, 67, 71
  Pettersson, 132–51
Alexander the Great, 5, 154, 160
American Miscellaneous Society, 201, 203
Amundsen, Roald, 118
Anchors, invention of, 6
Anderson, William, 95, 176–87
  first underice crossing of North Pole, 186–87
  nuclear submarine training, 179
  takes command of *Nautilus,* 182
Animals, marine, 33–35, 63
  Arctic Ocean, 86
  coloring, 63, 108–10, 159, 165–66
  deep sea, 63
  distribution at various depths, 50, 106–8
  eyes, 110–11
  transparent, 108–10

Antarctic
  Discovery I and *II,* 120–31
  early trips to, 116–17
  Scott's *Discovery* Expedition, 117–19
Antarctic Circle, 48
Antarctic expedition, 116–18
Aqualungs, 161–63
Arctic darkness, 83, 84
Arctic ocean
  blanket of ice, 92, 179, 182
  continental shelves in, 91–92
  current in, 76, 80, 92, 93, 95
  expeditions to
    Fram, 74–96
    Nautilus, 176–87
    Skate, 188–98
  ice fingers, 189, 195
  land masses, 81
  marine life, 82
  plant and animal life, 86
  pressure ridges, 76, 83, 182–83
  study of, 179
Assumption Island, 165
Astrolabe, 7
Aurora Borealis, 82
Azores, 44

Bailey, Professor, 28, 40
Bali, 146–47
Bancroft, George, 22
Barton, Otis, 154–56
Basalt, 212
Bascom, Willard, 199–215
  Mohole Project
    first tests, 206–13
    fomentation of, 200–206
    future plans for, 213–15
Bathyscaph, 145, 168–75
  built by Piccard, 168
  Challenger Deep dive, 172–74
  Trieste, 170–75
Bathysphere, 154–60
  Beebe's last dive, 157–59
  designed and built by Barton, 154–55
  first test dives, 155–56

Beebe, William, 154–60
  Director of the Department of Tropical
    Research of the New York Zoologi-
    cal Society, 155
  first bathysphere test, 155–56
  last dive, 157–60
Bering Straits, 184
Bermuda, 155
Berrill, N.J., 122
Biology, marine, 8–9, 32–53, 101
Blake, expeditions, 60–64
Blessing, Dr., 79, 86
Borings, 134, 137–48, 151, 201, 211–13
Bottom of the sea; see Floor of the ocean
Boyd, David, 196–97
British Museum, 97, 119
Brooke, John M., 27–30, 33, 60
  association with Matthew Maury, 27–29
  sounding device, 27–29
Buchanan, J. Y., 37, 45–46
Burke, Admiral Arleigh, 178, 185, 198

Calvert, James F., 95, 178–80, 188–98
  Drift Station Alpha, 191–93
  first surfacing of a submarine at the
    North Pole, 196
  maiden voyage of the Skate, 188–91
  nuclear submarine training, 180
  Surface at the Pole, 198
  winter crossing of the North Pole, 194–
    98
Calypso, laboratory ship, 166–67
Cape Chelyuskin, 78
Cape Fligely, 88
Cape Flora, 93
Cape of Good Hope, 8–9
Caribbean Sea, 61–63
Carpenter, W. B., 34
Challenger, 9, 31–53
  findings, 59–61, 64
  importance of, 52–53
  published results, 51–52, 98–101
  reliability of results, 98
  routes taken, 38–50
  specimens collected, 51
Challenger Deep, 50, 145, 172
Charts, 7, 46
  Maury's work, 19–22, 30
Christiania, University of, 96
Christiania Geographical Society, 76
Christmas Island, 103
Circulation of the sea, 25
Colors of marine animals, 63, 108–9, 159,
  165–66
Compasses, 7
  inertial navigation, 188–91

Continental shelf, 50, 91–92
Cook, Captain James, 8, 26, 116–17,
  143–44
Copepods, 129
Coral reefs, 42, 65, 67–71
Corers, sediment, 137–39, 151
Cousteau, Jacques-Yves, 100, 160–68
  discovery of ancient treasure, 164–65
  inventor of aqualung, 160–62
  The Silent World, 165, 168
  Undersea Diving Group, 163–64
  underwater photography, 165–66
Crabs, 43
Croyden expedition, 69
Crust of earth, 138, 201, 204, 213
  kind of rock, 201
  thickness of, 201
Currents, 24, 92, 95
  charts; see Charts
  temperatures, 92
CUSS I, 205–12
Cuttlefish, 107

Darwin, Charles, 25, 33, 57–58, 68–71,
  201
  Voyage of the Beagle, 68–69
Deacon, G. E. R., 131
Deep scattering layer, 46, 166
Deeps in ocean, 50, 104, 107, 172–75,
  205
  Atlantic Deep, 205
  Challenger Deep, 50, 172–75
DeLong, George W., 75
Depths of the ocean, 27, 50, 145
  Arctic soundings, 81
  deepest points, 103
  measuring, 28–29, 60
  Pacific Ocean, 145
Depths of the Ocean (Murray and
  Hjort), 104, 113
Diatoms, 85–86, 95
Diaz, Bartholomew, 8–9, 116
Dietz, Robert, 171–72
Discovery, Antarctic Expedition, 116–30
  Hardy's studies on
    krill, 126–29
    plankton, 129–30
    whales, 121, 124–27
Discovery II, 130–31
Diving apparatus, of Cousteau, 160
Diving suits, 5
Dredges and dredging, 34, 42, 61, 82
  taken by Nansen, 82
Drift Station Alpha, 191–93
Dumas, Frederic, 161, 163

Earthquakes and volcanic eruptions, 143, 147–48, 201–2
Earth's crust, 199–215
Easter Island, 71
Echo sounder, 137, 140–42, 145
Economy of the sea, 111
Eisenhower, Dwight D., 175, 187
Elie Monnier, 163–64
Emden Deep, 145
English, Dr. T. Saunders, 191
Eniwetok Islands, 71
Environment, adapting to, 98–99
Equipment, oceanographic, 10, 60–61, 64
Eyes of marine animals, 110–11

Falkland Islands, 48, 119, 122
Fargues, Maurice, 162
Faroe Channel, 51, 102
Faroe Islands, 92
Fathometers, 177, 182, 186
Field, Cyrus, 30
Fiji Islands, 70, 147
Fisheries, 92–93
Floor of the ocean, 28, 100, 104–5
    age of deposits on, 137, 141
    fish living on, 111
    life on, 33–53
    survey of, 140
Flying fish, 44
Food chain, 122, 128–29
Food resources of the sea, 133
Forbes, Edward, 33
Forminifera, 138
Fram expedition, 74–96
    description of ship, 77
    drift of, 84
    frozen in ice, 79–95
    release from ice, 95
    scientific investigations, 80–82, 85–86
Franz Josef Land, 88–89, 91, 95
French Diving Team, 160, 161

Gagnan, Emile, 160
Galapagos Island, 66, 71–72
Galley of Mahdia, 164–65
Geological history, 134, 136–39
Geology, oceanic, 151
Gibraltar, 45
Globigerina ooze, 28, 40–41, 61, 65–66, 105, 141, 211
Gran, H. H., 86, 111–13
Great Barrier Reef, 69–70
Great Britain, oceanic investigations, 35
Greenland, 75–76
Guadalupe Island, 204, 206–13
Gulf of Georgia, 56

Gulf Stream, 22–24, 62
Gyroscope, 183

Hardy, Sir Alister, 4–5, 107, 115–20
    Discovery II, 130–31
    The Open Sea, 46
    Scientific Director of *Discovery I* Expedition, 120–30
Harvard Museum, 57, 62, 64, 66–67, 72
Harvard University, 55–57
Hawaiian Islands, 143
Helland-Hansen, Bjorn, 107–10
Henry, Captain Thomas, 182
Henry the Navigator, Prince, 7–8, 116
Hensen, Victor, 41, 112
Herdman, William, 101
Herring, 108, 128–29
Hjort, John, 102–10
Hoover, Herbert, 96
Houston, General Sam, 13, 30
Humbolt Current, 71–72
Hummocks, 76, 83, 89, 179
Huxley, Thomas, 46, 57, 65

Ice, pressure of, 83
Icebergs, 131–32
Inaccessible Island, 66
Indian Ocean, 131, 147
Instruments, for oceanic research, 7–10, 137
International Council for the Exploration of the Sea, 98

Jackson, Senator Henry, 178
Jackson-Harmsworth Polar Expedition, 91
Jan Mayen, voyage to North, 101
Jan Mayen Island, 101, 182
Jeannette, ship, 75–76, 197
Jellyfish, 65, 108–9
Johansen, Hjalmar, 88–91

Kemp, Stanley, 120
Krill, 126–27, 129, 133
Kullenberg, Borja, 139–40, 151

Lafayette, Marquis de, 14–15
Lawrence, James, 58
League of Nations, 96
Light under water, 98, 156, 158
    effect on deep sea animals, 43–44
    intensities, 98–99, 108–10
Lill, Gordon, 200–201, 203
Living condition in sea, 33–53, 99–100, 105, 107
Lomonsosov mountain chain, 191

Longitudinal roulette, 183
Lowell, John, 55
Lowell Scientific School, 56
Lucky Thirteen, 74, 94
Lyon, Dr. Waldo, 177, 182, 183, 186

McWethy, Robert D., 177
Madeira Islands, 142
Magellan, 8, 26
Mantle of earth, 201, 204
Marine science, 9
Markham, Clement, 117
Martinique, 143
Maury, Matthew, 10–11, 12–31
  early life, 12–14
  naval service, 14–18, 30–31
  A New Theoretical Treatise on Navi-
    gation, 17
  The Physical Geography of the Sea, 22,
    26, 29, 33
  search for truth, 22
  theories, 22–29
  Wind and Current Charts, 19–22, 27,
    30, 46, 49
Mediterranean Sea, 147–49
Melville, Herman, 10
Meteors and meteoric dust, 150
Michael Sars Expedition, 98, 103–13
  equipment, 105–6
  study of ocean's layers, 104–12
Migration of fish
  vertical, 46–47
  whales, 123–25
Mindanao Trench, 145
Moho Discontinuity, 201–2, 213
Mohole project, 11, 199–215
  Cuss I, 205–13
  drilling techniques, 206–12
  future plans, 213–15
  planning by Bascom, 200–206
  sediment cores, 211–13
  sponsored by the American Miscella-
    neous Society, 203
Mohorovicic, Andriya, 201–2
Monad, Theodore, 169
Moseley, Henry, 47–50
Mount Vesuvius, 147, 148
Mountains under the sea, 142, 191
  Atlantic Ridge, 142
  Lomonsosov chain, 191
Murida fish, 43–44
Murray, Sir John, 67, 69–70, 97–114,
    117, 134, 136
  aboard the Challenger, 37–38, 40–42,
    52, 98–102
  early life, 100–01

editing of Challenger Reports, 113
  Michael Sars expedition, 103–4

Nansen, Fridtjof, 74–96, 185, 193
  aboard the Windward, 93
  accomplishments, 95–96
  dredgings, 82
  education, 75–76
  Farthest North, 96
  Nobel Peace Prize given to, 96
  pressure of ice, 83
  return to Norway, 93–94
  scientific observations, 80–82, 85–86
  trek to the Pole, 88–89
  trip back, 89–91
  water bottle invented by, 80, 96
National Science Foundation, 204–5
Nautilus, nuclear submarine, 86, 95, 176–
    78, 180–87
  first trip by ship to North Pole, 182–87
  use of name, 176, 177, 178
Navigation, 7, 88
  celestial, 190
  charts, 7, 19–22, 30, 46
  inertial, 188–91
Nero Deep, 103, 172
Newfoundland Banks, 92
Nobel Peace Prize, 96
North Polar Sea, 95
North Pole, 118–19
  Nansen's expedition, 74–96
  Nautilus and Skate trips to, 176–98
  sea route, 95
Norway, oceanic research sponsored by,
    76, 102
Nuclear submarines, 180–83, 189

Oceanography, 3–4, 9–10, 86, 152
Oil drilling techniques, 205–10
Ooze, 61, 65–66, 105, 141, 211
  analysis of, 28, 40–41
  globigerina, 41, 61, 105, 141, 211
  importance of, 41, 105
  other kinds of, 41
Oxygen, presence in sea water, 99

Pacific Isles, 143–46
Pacific Ocean, 144–45
  dredging and sounding, 65
  exploring, 103, 168–75
  how formed, 144
Panama, Isthmus of, 63, 65
Panama Canal Zone, 143
Pathfinder of the Sea (Matthew Maury),
    31
Peary, Robert Edwin, 118, 177

Penguins, 47
Periscope, 183, 190
Pettersson, Hans, 134–52
  corings, 137–42, 145–51
  Director of the Swedish Deep Sea Expedition, 136–51
  early life, 135–42
Pettersson-Nansen water bottle, 96
Phosphates, 103
Phosphorescence, 81, 109–10
Photography, underwater, 162–63, 165–68
Phyla, 100
Piccard, Auguste
  first dive, 169
  invention of the bathyscaph, 168
Piccard, Jacques
  Challenger Deep dive, 172–74
  and the Trieste, 170–74
Piggott, C. S., 138
Pirates, 7
Piston core sampler, 139, 140
Plankton, 41, 66, 111–13
  collecting, 41–42, 47
  foraminifera, 138
  Gran, H. H., study of plankton, 111–13
  importance in economy of sea, 111
  krill, 126–27, 129, 133
  luminescence of, 109, 159
  Nansen's taking of, 81, 85
  in polar currents, 92–93
  recorder devices, 127–28
  survey, 128, 132
Plants, marine, 111
Polar currents, 92, 95
Polar expeditions, 74–96
Polar regions, explosion of life, 92–93
Polar ice, 75
Polar Sea, 75
Pollen-analytical method, 149
Polynya, 180, 185, 189, 190–192
Polynesian Islands, 71
Portuguese expeditions, 7–8
Pressure ridges, 75, 83, 181, 185
Pressures, 99
  deep sea, 46
  ice, 83
  rate of increase, 99
  on Trieste at bottom of ocean, 173
Puerto Rico, 204
Pullar, Frederick, 102
Pullar, Laurence, 102
Pytheas, Greek explorer, 6

Radioactive elements, 137, 146, 148–49
Rapture, deep sea, 161–62

Ready, 155–59
Red clay, on ocean floor, 104–5, 141
Research, oceanographic, 9–10, 98
Revelle, Roger, 68, 115, 166, 200
Rickover, Admiral Hyman G., 178–80, 182, 198
Ridges, submarine, 102, 137
Ross, James Clark, 117
Ross Sea, 117
Routes, sea, 20
Royal Society of London, 9, 32, 34, 65

St. Paul's Rocks, 47, 213–14
Salts in the sea, 24–26
Salvage work, 163–64
Sandwich Islands, 144
Sargasso Sea, 108–9
Sargassum, 44–45
Sars, Michael, 34, 36
Scotland, sea lochs, 102
Scott, Robert Falcon, 117–19
Scripps Institution of Oceanography, 115, 166, 200–213
Sea, definition, 3–4
Sea anemones, 65
Sea butterflies (pteropods), 40
Sea cucumbers, 43
Sea lilies, 62
Sea routes, shortening of, 20
Sea snow, 112, 173
Sea urchins, 57, 59, 62
Seaweed, 44–45
Sediment, 42
  cores, 134, 137–48, 151, 211–13
Sedimentation, rate, 150
Seven Miles Down (Jacques Piccard), 171
Sextant, 7
Shackleton, Ernest, 118
Sharks, 107
Shrimps, 43–44, 107
Silent World, The (Cousteau), 165, 168
Skate, nuclear submarine, 86, 95, 176–78, 181, 188–98
  second trip to the Pole, 194–96
Sledge dogs, 78, 87, 89, 90
Sound transmission, 171, 192, 202
Sound waves, rate of travel, 140
Sounding devices, 28–29, 60–61, 81
Sounds, 166, 171
South Georgia, 119, 121
South Pole, 117–19
South Sea Islands, 68
Spanish expedition, 7–8
Sponges, 43
Squids, 107
Starfish, 57, 59, 62

Steffansson, Vilhjalmur, 191
Steinbeck, John, 202, 207, 209–12
Straits of Magellan, 48
Studies, oceanic, 4
Sunken ships, exploring, 163–65
Superstitions, 4, 6–8
Surface at the Pole (Calvert), 198
Sverdrup, Otto, 75, 77–78, 87–88, 94–95
Swedish Deep Sea Expedition, 135–51

Telephone communications, 156, 174
Temperatures of the sea, 35, 50, 80–81, 99
Ternate, 146
Theory of earth's layers, 201
Thermocline, 172
Thermometers, 35
  Pettersson-Nansen water bottle, 80–81, 96
Thomson, Wyville, 9, 32–53, 100, 102
  Agassiz and, 58–59, 62–64
  The Depths of the Sea, 35
  Director of the *Challenger* Expedition Commission, 51
  early life, 35–36
  marine research, 36
  objectives of expedition, 50
  range of investigations, 38–39
  routes taken, 38–50
  Voyage of the Challenger, 51
Thomson Ridge, 102
Tides, 6
Transatlantic cable, 9, 26, 30, 33–34
Transparent animals, 108–10
Trieste, 170–74
  bought by the United States Office of Naval Research, 171
  Challenger Deep dive, 172–75
  first dives, 69–70

Trinidad, 160
Triton, 102
Tyrrhenian Sea, 147, 170

Underwater diving, 161
United States
  Coast Survey, 56–57, 60
  Fish Commission, 64, 65
  Hydrographic Office, 18, 31
  Naval Academy, 17–18, 22, 31
  Office of Naval Research, 171–72, 205

Vertical migration of animals, 46, 166
Volcanic eruptions, 142, 143

Walsh, Don, 172–75
Water, study of layers of, 137
West Indies, 142–43
Westward Ho with the Albatross (Pettersson), 148
Whales, 93, 107, 116, 119–32
  breeding habits, 125–26
  food of, 122, 126–27, 129
  migrations, 123–25
  regulation of whaling industry, 120
  tagging, 123–24
  types of, 121–22
Wilkins, Sir Hubert, 177, 178, 193–97
Wilkinson, Eugene, 178–79, 182
William Scoresby, 121, 123–24, 132
Wilson, Dr. E. A., 118
Windward, British ship, 92–93
Wittmann, Walt, 190
Worms, sea, 107
  Bololo, 71

Yucatan Banks, 61